# The
# Fire Brigade Hand|
# Special Appliances - Volume 1

# The Fire Brigade Handbook - Special Appliances - Volume 1

The Fire Brigade Handbook - Special Appliances Volume 1 - is a directory of fire appliances manufactured for use by the various fire authorities in England, Scotland and Wales and follows on from the much acclaimed Handbook of current fire brigade appliances also published by British Bus Publishing. The form describes the fleet number, registration and type, together with the most recent station to which it was allocated. Invariably appliances move from time to time to meet the demands placed on the brigades.

This is the first of two volumes dedicated to the special appliances such as turntable ladders, emergency tenders and covers production details from the rare to the numerous of each type under the chassis class.

Obtaining the comprehensive information for this book has been a major task. This is the first attempt at publishing a pair of books of its type and covers specialist appliances from the early 1920's. In a lot of cases very little information is available so I have had to accept some information in good faith, and I have made it as accurate as I have been able to ascertain. I therefore would welcome any additional information and photographic material which would help in future publications.

.

Principal Editor: Clive Shearman

**Acknowledgments:**
I am grateful to the invaluable assistance of a number of people in the preparation of this publication . The Late Alan Batchelor, Mike Bunn, Norman Downs, Les Edkins, Roy Goodey , Ron Henderson, The Late John Hughes, Michael Lawmon, Ian Moore, Ken Reid, Steve Shaw, David Thomas and Keith Wardell for the use of their excellent photographic and slide collections. Finally special mention for Ron Henderson and Ian Moore, who both did hundreds of hours of proof reading and gave valuable advice, assistance and encouragement

ISBN 1 897990 49 9 (Volume 1)
ISBN 1 897990 50 2 (Volume 2)

Published by *British Bus Publishing* Ltd
The Vyne, 16 St Margarets Drive, Wellington,
Telford, Shropshire, TF1 3PH
© British Bus Publishing, September 1997

*Frontispiece:* This AEC Regal Merryweather Ladder, LYB388, was delivered in 1950 to the Somerset Fire Brigade, and was to serve at Milton Street in Weston super mare for the rest of its time. In 1974 the station became part of the County of Avon Fire Brigade. At the end of its fire service duties the machine went, like many other ladders, to a tree surgeon for further service. *Michael Lawmon*

# CONTENTS

# KEY

| Reg No | Fleet No | TYPE | YR | OS | BRIGADE | Details/Stations |
|---|---|---|---|---|---|---|
| **Example** | | | | | | |
| **NPA250** | **TL4P** **MW-144** | **TLP** | **49** | **69** | **Surrey County Council Fire Brigade** | **Kingston St-Wimbledon-1965** **K21 Kingston St-Wimbledon-1966** **Reserve-1969** **100'L/London Fire Brigade** |

| Reg No | Fleet No | | YR | OS | | Details/Stations |
|---|---|---|---|---|---|---|
| **NPA250** | | | | | | Vehicle Registration Number |
| | **Fleet No** | | | | | |
| | **TL4P** **MW-144** | | | | | Vehicle Fleet or Code Number Merryweather Ladder Production No |
| | | **Type** | | | | |
| | | **TL/P** | | | | Type of Appliance-Turntable Ladder See Appliance Code List |
| | | | **YR** | | | |
| | | | **49** | | | Year put into service-1949 |
| | | | | **OS** | | |
| | | | | **69** | | Year taken out of service-1969 |
| | | | | | **BRIGADE** | |
| | | | | | **Surrey County Council Fire Brigade** | Original purchasing Brigade/City/ County Borough. These ceased to exist in the England & Wales in 1974. In Scotland the changeover took place in 1975. |
| | | | | | | **Details/Station** |
| | | | | | | Kingston St-Wimbledon was the original allocation for this vehicle. In 1965 it became K21 (**the station code number**) Wimbledon of the London Fire Brigade. Some machines will have the letters **Re-ch- (Re-chassied)** this applies to earlier bodies or ladders/booms being put onto later chassis types. |

# INTRODUCTION

My interest in Fire Appliances of all types started back in the sixties when, as a youngster, I saw some Middlesex machines at a Road Traffic Accident on Slade's Hill, in North London, where I used to live. I can still see those firemen getting out of the pump and the emergency tender and I wondered where the men and machines came from? It would take many years and many thousands of hours of research to bring an answer to the question.

I first started taking a serious interest in my hobby in 1980 when I started photographing machines at various locations. I would visit stations and wonder what type of appliance used to serve there in bygone days. This is where my interest in compiling records and collecting lists started and where the Fire Brigade Specialist Appliance Handbook was ultimately born.

One of the latest arivals with Hampshire Fire and Rescue Service is this attractive Volvo FL10 with bodywork provided by Angloco of Batley in West Yorkshire. The appliance is shown prior to delivery which was just prior to our going to press with this first volume of special fire appliances.
*Angloco Limited*

When I started the project in 1991 its purpose was to give me a comprehensive listing of all Specialist Appliances which served across the whole of the United Kingdom from the early days of motorisation to the present day. I have had many thousands of hours stuck in front of my computer typing out lists and letters to various sources too numerous to mention. I have followed certain lines of investigation which have thrown up blanks, but many, many friends have dug out old information and lists which have proved invaluable. My main hope is that it will prove a catalyst for people to dig out information which I have missed so that future updates can give us a complete historical reference.

This is the first known publication of its type, and follows in the fine tradition of the previous Fire Brigade Handbooks which have given a valuable insight into the Modern Fire Service. My publication covers the so called Specialist Appliances, the Turntable Ladders, Emergency Tenders, Hydraulic Platforms and the numerous other types that back up the front line pumping appliances. Finally, to answer the question I asked myself all those years ago, the pump was a Dennis F8 and came from Enfield, and the emergency tender was a Commer QX and came from Edmonton.

**YAG470X was supplied to Humberside Fire Service in 1981 as the rescue tender based at Hull West fire station. Wearing an all-white livery it is a Reynolds Boughton 4x4 with Angloco bodywork.**
*Norman Downs*

# AEC

| Reg No | Fleet No | TYPE | YR | OS | Appliance & Brigade Name | Details/Stations |
|---|---|---|---|---|---|---|
| | Merry'r Ladder No MW- | | | | **AEC REGAL Turntable Ladders** | The Regal bus chassis was used to mount the 4 section Merryweather ladder. The Regal was powered by a 9.5 litre Meadows petrol engine. Where fitted they had 500 or 800gpm pumps. |
| | | | | | | **There were a total of 10 Home Office orders supplied at £6,986 each. Ordered for 29/4/1947.** |
| NPA250 | 55TLP TL4P MW-144 | TLP | 49 | 69 | Surrey County Council Fire Brigade | Kingston St-Wimbledon-1965 K21 Kingston St-Wimbledon-1966 /Reserve-1969 100'L/London Fire Brigade |
| CMS507 | MW-145 | TLP | 49 | 68 | Central Area Fire Brigade (Scotland) | S8 Rannoch Rd-Stirling-1968 /100'L |
| KTF847 | MW-146 | TL | 49 | 67 | Lancashire County Fire Brigade | E73 Wellington Rd-Ashton under Lyne-1965 Reserve-1967/100'L |
| FVA2 | MW-147 | TLP | 49 | 68 | Lanarkshire Fire Brigade (Scotland) | E1 Bothwill Rd-Hamilton-1968 /100'L **Sold to Window Cleaning Firm** |

AEC Regal/ Merryweather 100' Turntable Ladder NPA250 was delivered to Wimbledon in 1949. This machine, which was one of a pair, served there till 1965 when boundary changes took it from Surrey to London Fire Brigade control. *Keith Wardell collection*

| | | | | | | |
|---|---|---|---|---|---|---|
| LYB388 | MW-148 | TLP | 50 | 75 | Somerset Fire Brigade | Weston Super Mare-1960 Milton St-Weston Super Mare-1974    C1 Milton St-Weston Super Reserve-1974/100'L    Never operational for County of Avon Fire Brigade    **Sold to Universal Cleaners-Worcestershire** |
| KRH806 | MW-149 | TLP | 50 | 76 | City of Kingston upon Hull Fire Brigade | A1 Worship St-Hull Central-1961 A2 Clough Rd-Hull North-1974 A3 Calvert Lane-Hull West-1976/100'l Humberside Fire Brigade/**Preserved** |
| NPJ750 | 56TLP TL5P MW-150 | TLP | 50 | 71 | Surrey County Council Fire Brigade | Richmond Rd-Kingston-1965 K31 Richmond Rd-Kingston 1969 Reserve-1971/100'L London Fire Brigade/**Sold to Rowntrees (York)/Preserved** |
| KNY14 | MW-151 | TLP | 50 | 72 | Glamorgan County Fire Brigade (Wales) | 4 Commercial Rd-Port Talbot-1972 Glamorgan County FB 100'L/**Scrapped 1980** |
| LTF716 | MW-152 | TL | 50 | 67 | Lancashire County Fire Brigade | F80/D70 Manchester Rd-Accrington-1965  Reserve-1967/100'L |
| KOM798 | 75 MW-153 | TLP | 51 | 65 | City of Birmingham | A1 Lancaster Circus-Central-1965-Birmingham **Sold to Mackay's a Scottish construction firm** 100'L/**Preserved** |

| | | | | | | |
|---|---|---|---|---|---|---|
| | | | | | **AEC REGENT Turntable Ladders** | **The Regent bus chassis with its low centre of gravity for double decked buses proved an ideal platform for a Turntable Ladder. It was powered by the 9.6 litre Meadows petrol engine. It had the 4 section light alloy hydraulic ladder.** |
| JUN104 | MW-154 | TLP | 53 | 78 | Denbigh & Montgomeryshire FB (Wales) | 2 Abergale Rd-Colwyn Bay-1974 E1 Bradley Rd-Wrexham-1978 /Reserve-1979/100'L **Preserved**-County of Clwyd Fire Service **FWC Regent-AEC Regal shape** |
| 181BNU | | TLP | 56 | 72 | Derbyshire Fire Service | B1 Campton Drive-Buxton-1971 /Reserve-1972 Merryweather-100'L |
| YKP177 | 52TL TL7 | TLP | 57 | 72 | Kent Fire Brigade | A Div South St-Bromley-1965 /H21 South St-Bromley-1970 Reserve-1972/London Fire Brigade **Ladders off Merryweather Meadows-EKP395-100'L This appliance also had a 11.3 litre petrol engine, hence the deep radiator front to accommodate the large engine . Preserved** /Merryweather 100'L |
| JFS372 | MW-15 | TLP | 58 | 77 | South Eastern Area Fire Brigade (Scotland) | Lauriston Place-Edingburgh-1958 Leith-Edingburgh-1975 South Eastern AFB-Reserve-1977 Lothian & Borders Fire Brigade **Ladders off Leyland TLM2-Merryweather-DSF140** |
| GFB712 | | TLP | 58 | 70 | City of Bath Fire Brigade | Cleveland Bridge-City of Bath-1967 Reserve-1970 **Ladders off Merryweather Meadows-GL4110-100'L** |
| KSG977 | MW-22 | TLP | 59 | 74 | South Eastern Area Fire Brigade (Scotland) | Stockbridge-Edingburgh Reserve/100'L/**Preserved** **Ladders off Merryweather Dorman-WS3074** |

*Above:* **The City of Bath operated GFB712, an AEC Regent with re-chassied Merryweather ladders from an earlier Leyland TLM appliance which also served at the Cleveland Bridge station. Delivered in 1958 it was replaced in 1967 by an AEC Mercury TGM Merryweather**.
*Keith Wardell collection*

*Left:* **A fine example of the AEC Regent chassis with Merryweather ladders. YKP177 is a 1957 Bromley/Kent-based appliance that found itself in the fleet of the London Fire Brigade after boundary changes in 1965. It was unusual in that the bonnet contained a larger than normal engine.**
*The late Alan Batchelor*

| | MW-No New Type Ladder | | | | AEC MERCURY Turntable Ladders | The Mercury heavy goods chassis with certain adaptions proved along with its low centre of gravity an ideal platform for aerial appliances. The ladder apart from a few exceptions was the 4 section, Hydraulically operated Merryweather. Later it was fitted to the Mercury TGM chassis with the Ergomatic tilt-cab. |
|---|---|---|---|---|---|---|
| | | | | | | **MW-Merryweather Ladder No**<br>Missing numbers were ladders which were exported to be mounted onto a foreign chassis. |
| OVY200 | 4<br>MW-1 | TL | 57 | 83 | City of York | Clifford St-York-1974 SD 1 Clifford St-York<br>North Yorkshire Fire Brigade<br>**Ladder Re-ch onto S&DrewryWY/G&T Power-YVN67Y** |
| WEL847 | MW-2 | TLP | 57 | 82 | Boturnemouth Fire Brigade | Holdenhurst Rd-Bournemouth-1974 B24 Holdenhurst Rd-Bournemouth-Dorset FB-1982/**Preserved Worcestershire** |
| VND217 | MW-3 | TLP | 57 | 76 | City of Manchester | #2 Wilmslow Rd-Withington-1974 Reserve<br>Greater Manchester CFS-1976 |
| RFS132 | MW-4 | TL | 57 | 88 | South Eastern Area Fire Brigade (Scotland) | Lauriston Place-Edinburgh-1975 /30 Lauriston Place-1976-Lothian & Borders FB/Reserve-1984/**Preserved** |
| CHG1 | MW-5 | TLP | 57 | 74 | Burnley County Borough FB | Manchester Rd-Burnley-1965 Belvidere Rd-Burnley-1974<br>**Sold to G&T Attack as Spare TL** |
| YKF719 | E10<br>MW-6 | TLP | 57 | 82 | City of Liverpool | 6 Banks Rd-Liverpool-1962<br>13 Storington Ave-Liverpool-1967 Training Centre-1982<br>**Ladder Re-ch onto Dennis F125/Dennis-ACM390/404X-?** |
| OWM261 | MW-7 | TLP | 57 | 76 | Southport County Borough FB | Manchester Rd-Southport-1974 Reserve-Merseyside FB-1976    Ladder Re-chassied onto Dennis F125/Dennis **DWM603Y Single cab version.** |
| LES448 | MW-8 | TL | 57 | 85 | Perth & Kinross Fire Brigade (Scotland) | High St-Perth-1975 B1-Perth-Tayside FB-1985<br>**Ladder onto Dodge G16C/G&T Power-B157USR** |
| PKU833 | MW-9 | TLP | 58 | 82 | City of Bradford | Nelson St-Bradford-1974 - **Named 'Benjamin W Berry'**<br>A11 Bradford-West Yorkshire FS 1982<br>**Ladder onto Dennis F125/G&T Power-MWX201V** |
| 404KNU | MW-11 | TL | 58 | 85 | Derbyshire Fire Service | B3 Charlestown Rd-Glossop-Derbyshire FS<br>**Sold to Essex CFB for ladder re-chassis-never used.** |
| PRX62 | MW-13 | TLP | 58 | 81 | Reading & Berkshire Fire Brigade | Caversham Rd-Reading-1974 Caversham Rd-Royal Berkshire FB  **Ladder Re-chassied off Leyland TD7-GLW420**                    **Preserved** |
| 4TMX | TL-8/TL9<br>MW-14 | TL | 58 | 80 | Middlesex Fire Brigade | B39 Harrow Rd-Wembley-1966<br>E22 Blissett St-Greenwich-1980  London FB |
| KDJ404 | MW-16 | TLP | 58 | 78 | St Helens County Borough FB | 1 Parr Stocks Rd-St Helens CB-1974<br>E1 St Helens-Merseyside FB-1978<br>**Ladder Re-chassied onto Dennis F125/Dennis-A49HKC** |
| 10TMX | TL10/TL11<br>MW-17 | TL | 58 | 80 | Middlesex Fire Brigade | A7 Conway Rd-Tottenham-1965<br>J25 Tottenham-1972 /D22 Gunnersbury Lane-Acton-1980 London FB |
| 9TMX | TL9/TL10<br>MW-18 | TL | 58 | 80 | Middlesex Fire Brigade | C65 London Rd-Heston-1965<br>D27 London Rd-Heston-1972 /Reserve-1980-London FB |
| XGG945 | MW-19 | TLP | 58 | 60 | Glasgow Fire Service (Scotland) | A1 Ingram St-Central-1960<br>**Destroyed at the Whiskey Bond Fire - Cheapside Street 28/03/60** |
| 6708EV | MW-20 | TLP | 59 | 82 | Essex County Fire Brigade | High St-Leytonstone-1965 /D70 Fourth Ave-Harlow-1981<br>**Ladder onto S&D WY/G&T Power-ANO169X** |
| JCM61 | 1018<br>MW-21 | TL | 59 | 82 | Birkenhead County Borough (Merseyside) | Whetstone Lane-Birkenhead-1974<br>W1 Exmouth St-Birkenhead-Merseyside FB-1982<br>**Re-ch ladder off Leyland TLM2 Merryweather-BG6246** |
| VYE234 | 34TLP<br>TL8 | TLP | 59 | 81 | LCC London Fire Brigade | D63-Wolesley St-Dockhead-1965 / B24 Dockhead-1972<br>K24 Trinity Rd-Tooting-1981/Magirus 100'L **Sold to Rentokil Re-ch L off Dennis Morris/Magirus-GT6694/Preserved** |

| | | | | | | |
|---|---|---|---|---|---|---|
| 70GHW | MW-23 | TL | 59 | 79 | City of Bristol | #1 Bridwell St-Bristol-1967 /# 3 St Andrews Rd-Avonmouth-1973 /C1 Milton Ave Weston Super Mare-1978/Reserve-1979 County of Avon FB |
| HHF84 | MW-24 | TL | 59 | 79 | County Borough of Wallasey (Merseyside) | Mill Lane-Wallasey-1974 W6 Mill Lane-Wallasey-Merseyside FB-1979 **Ladder Re-chassied onto Dennis F125/Dennis-B925KWM** |
| 9760WJ | MW-25 | TLP | 59 | 77 | City of Sheffield | #4 Mansfield Rd-Sheffield-        /#2 Darnall Rd-Sheffield-1974  E1 Darnall Rd-Sheffield-South Yorkshire CFS/**Preserved** |
| RHS180 | MW-28 | TL | 59 | 80 | Western Area Fire Brigade (Scotland) | Canal St-Paisley-1974 /C4 Paisley-1980-Strathclyde FB **Ladder Re-ch onto S&Drewry WY/G&T Power NHS993V** |
| RHV802 | 50TL/TL15 MW-29 | TLP | 59 | 80 | East Ham County Borough FB | Prince Regent Lane-Plaistow-1965 L30-Plaistow-1980-London FB |
| MJX470 | MW-30 | TL | 59 | 80 | Halifax County Borough FB | Skircoat Moor Rd-Halifax-1974 B11 Halifax-1980-West Yorkshire FS **Ladder Re-ch onto  S&D WY/G&T Power-PNW625W** |
| TAN149 | 49TLP/TL14P MW-31 | TLP | 60 | 79 | West Ham County Borough FB | F21 Romford Rd-Stratford-1965/F21 Stratford-1972 C21 Old St-Shoreditch-London Fire Brigade **Ladder Re-chassied off Dennis/Merryweather-AJD324** |
| 513BGE | MW-32 | TLP | 60 | 68 | Glasgow Fire Service (Scotland) | A1 Ingram St-Central-1960-Ladders destroyed at **Cheapside   Conv to Hydraulic Platform with Simon SS65 Booms-1968** |
| 514BGE | MW-33 | TLP | 60 | 80 | Glasgow Fire Service (Scotland) | B1 Govan Rd-Govan-Glasgow-1975 B2 Govan-1980-Strathclyde FB **L  Re -ch onto S& Drewry WY/G&T Power-NHS992V** |
| 2599MV | TL11/TL12 MW-34 | TL | 60 | 79 | Middlesex Fire Brigade | B35 The Boroughs-Hendon-1965 /G24  Hendon-London FB **Preserved** |
| 2600MV | TL12/TL13 MW-35 | TL | 60 | 80 | Middlesex Fire Brigade | C62 Gunnersbury Lane-Acton-1965 D22 Acton-1972 J25 Loys Rd-Tottenham-1980/London FB **Ladders Re-chassied off Dennis/Merryweather-LME418** |
| XJN618 | MW-36 | TL | 60 | 84 | Southend on Sea County Borough FB | London Rd-Southend CBFB-1964 Sutton Rd-Southend-1974 BD 30 Southend-Essex County FB **L  Re-ch  onto Dennis F125/G&T Power-RVW852W** |
| 1827NC | MW-37 | TLP | 60 | 78 | City of Manchester | London Rd-Manchester-1974  Reserve-Greater Manchester CFS-1978/**Sold to M .Luce-Tree Surgeon's-Worcester** |
| 7981BT | MW-40 | TL | 60 | 86 | East Riding of Yorkshire Fire Brigade | 2 Bessingby Rd-Bridlington-1974 /B3 Bridlington-1976 B1 Southcoates Rd-Hull East-1984/Res-1986/ Humberside FB **Sold M. Luce Tree Surgeon-Worcester/Re-reg PSU404** |
| MTS279 | MW-41 | TL | 59 | 85 | Angus Area Fire Brigade (Scotland) | Strathmore Ave-Dundee-1975 A2 Strathmore Ave-Tayside FB-1985 |
| 1BVA | MW-43 | TL | 60 | 88 | Lanarkshire Fire Brigade (Scotland) | Bothwell Rd-Hamilton-1975 /E1 Hamilton-1980 A3 Springburn-1988 /Strathclyde FB Reserve-1988 |
| VJY44 | 50-4 MW-44 | TL | 60 | 81 | City of Plymouth | Greenbank Rd-Greenbank-Plymouth-1974 W50 Greenbank-Devon FB-1981-**Sold to G&T Power Ladders Re-ch S& Drewry  WY/G&T Power-NTA751W** |
| 7407AT | MW-45 | TL | 60 | 86 | City of Kingston upon Hull FB | #1 Worship St-Hull-1974  A1-Worship St-Hull Central-Humberside FB-1984/Reserve-1986-**Refurbished by G&T** |
| SBR754 | MW-47 | TLP | 60 | 79 | Sunderland Fire Brigade | #1 Dun Cow St-Sunderland-1974 N Sunderland-Tyne & Wear MFB-1979 |
| OXG950 | 5 MW-49 | TL | 61 | 81 | Middlesbrough County Borough FB | 1 Park Road South-Middlesbrough-1968-Teesside FB 4 Trunk Rd-Redcar-1974 / Redcar-1981-Cleveland CFB **Ladder Re-ch Dennis F125/G&T POWER-JDC296W** |
| 194SBB | MW-50 | TL | 61 | 79 | Newcastle & Gateshead Fire Brigade | A1 Pilgrim St-Newcastle-1966 /B1 Dryden Rd-Gateshead-1974  V Gateshead-1975-Tyne & Wear MFB Reserve-1979 |
| 235CXP | 35TLP/TL17P MW-51 | TLP | 61 | 82 | LCC London Fire Brigade | A21 Chiltern St-Manchester Square-1972 D27-London Rd-Heston-1980 /London FB |

**Appliance 236CXP is one of the few AEC Mercury chassis to be delivered with Magirus Ladders. This 1961 vintage turntable ladder was new to station B22 Lambeth in London but moved to see service at E22 East Greenwich. Of interest is the old LCC crest on the passenger door. In 1965 London came under Greater London Council control**. *Keith Wardell collection*

| 22ML | TL13/TL16 MW-53 | TL | 61 | 80 | Middlesex Fire Brigade | C71 Shepistone Lane-Hayes-1965 /D30 Hayes London FB-1980 |
|---|---|---|---|---|---|---|
| VBA187 | MW-54 | TL | 61 | 78 | City of Salford | #1 The Crescent-Salford-1974 A10 Salford-Greater Manchester CFS-1978-**Preserved** |
| RRN999 | 259 MW-55 | TL | 61 | 83 | Preston County Borough FB | Tithbarn St-Preston-1962 /Blackpool Rd-Preston-1974 C50 Preston-Lancashire CFB-1980 |
| 636CUA | MW-57 | TLP | 61 | 84 | Leeds City Fire Brigade | Dewsbury Rd-Hunslett-Leeds-1974 E11 Hunslett-1984-West Yorkshire FS/**Preserved** |

| | | | | | | |
|---|---|---|---|---|---|---|
| 5724MN | MW-58 | TLP | 61 | 87 | Isle of Man Fire Brigade | 1 Peel Rd-Douglas |
| 169PFC | 6 MW-59 | TLP | 61 | 84 | City of Oxford | Rewley Rd-Oxford-1974 <br> B01 Rewley Rd-Oxford-1984 Oxfordshire Fire Service |
| 909RDH | | TL | 62 | 80 | Walsall County Borough FB | Blue Lane West-Walsall-1974 <br> H01/E1 Blue Lane West-Walsall /Haydon-Magirus 100'L <br> **Ladders Re-chassied onto Ford D1114-Carmichael-EBP334W- Reading &Berkshire FB** |
| CBY1 | TL19 MW-65 | TLP | 62 | | LCC London Fire Brigade | Old Town-Croydon-1965/ K21 Kingston Rd-Wimbledon-1981 **Preserved by London FB for ceremonial's and funeral's.** |
| 8126FD | 185 MW-67 | TL | 62 | 82 | Dudley County Borough FB | Tower St-Dudley-1974 <br> F01-D9 Tower St-Dudley /West Midlands FS/ **Preserved** |
| 3624FM | MW-70 | TLP | 63 | 81 | City of Chester | St Annes St-Chester-1974 <br> A1 Chester -Cheshire FB-1981 |
| 33MDT | MW-71 | TLP | 63 | 86 | Doncaster County Borough FB | Ledger Way-Doncaster-1974 <br> B1 Ledger Way-1981/Reserve-1986 /South Yorkshire CFS |
| 749SWC | MW-72 | TLP | 63 | 82 | Essex County Fire Brigade | A2/A10 Cowdray Ave-Colchester-Essex County FB |
| 750SWC | MW-73 | TLP | 63 | 84 | Essex County Fire Brigade | D48/B34 Rainsford Ave-Chelmsford-Essex County FB <br> **Ladder Re-ch onto S& Drewry WY/G&T P- A344MVX** |
| YDB469 | | TL | 63 | 80 | Stockport County Borough FB | #1 Whithill St-Stockport-1974 / D40 Whitehill St-1976 <br> D41 King St-Stockport-1980-Greater Manchester FS <br> **Haydon-Magirus-100'L** |
| 65KGA | | TL | 63 | 81 | Glasgow Fire Service (Scotland) | C1 Kelbourne St-North West-1968 <br> B1 Centre St-South-1974 /B1 South-1979 <br> B05 Queens Park-1981/ Strathclyde Fire Brigade <br> **Haydon-Magirus-100'L** |
| 237FLM | 37TLP/TL20P MW-74 | TLP | 63 | 81 | LCC London Fire Brigade | A5 Shaftsbury Ave-Soho-1965 <br> A24 Soho-1981/**Preserved** |
| 238FLM | 38TLP/TL21P MW-75 | TLP | 63 | 79 | LCC London Fire Brigade | B30 Commercial Rd-Whitechapel-1965 <br> C24-Whitechapel-1979 |
| 239FLM | 39TLP/TL22P MW-76 | TLP | 63 | 81 | LCC London Fire Brigade | B35 Cannon St-1965 <br> F22 East India Dock Rd-Poplar-1981/**Preserved** |
| 240FLM | 40TLP/TL23P MW-77 | TLP | 63 | 84 | LCC London Fire Brigade | C40 Queens Rd-New Cross-1972 <br> K21 West Hill-Wandsworth-1984/**Preserved** |
| 241FLM | 41TLP/TL24P MW-78 | TLP | 63 | 85 | LCC London Fire Brigade | D66 Gresham Rd-Brixton-1965 <br> B30-Brixton-1981/Reserve-1985 |
| 242FLM | 42TLP/TL25P MW-79 | TLP | 63 | 81 | LCC London Fire Brigade | D70 West Hill-Wandsworth-1965 <br> K21 Wandsworth-1972/B24 Wolesley St-Dockhead-1981 |
| RYJ949 | MW-80 | TL | 63 | 89 | Angus Area Fire Brigade (Scotland) | West Bell St-Central-Dundee-1970 Blackness Rd-Dundee-1975 /A1 Blackness Rd-1981-Tayside FB Reserve-1989 |
| 2934RA | MW-82 | TL | 64 | 84 | Derbyshire Fire Service | A1 Derby Rd-Ilkeston-Derbyshire Fire Service |
| LHD26 | MW-83 | TLP | 64 | 85 | Dewsbury County Borough FB | Huddersfield Rd-Dewsbury-1974/ C14 Huddersfield Rd-1982    C12 Carlinghow Lane-Batley-1985-West Yorkshire FS |
| BCH123B | MW-84 | TL | 64 | 83 | Derby County Borough Fire Brigade | #3 Kingsway-Derby-1974 /D3 Kingsway-Derby-Derbyshire FS **L Re-ch onto S& Drewry WY/G&T Power-VRC995Y** |
| 511HCY | MW-86 | TLP | 64 | 86 | City of Swansea (Wales) | Grove Place-Swansea-1974 /5 Swansea-West Glamorgan FS-1986 /**Preserved-re-registered-BSV920** |
| 8100GZ | MW-88 | TLP | 64 | 85 | Belfast Fire Brigade (Northern Ireland) | Ardoyne Fire Station-Belfast- Northern Ireland <br> **Ladder Re-chassied Dennis Delta 2/Dennis-PIA6875** |
| MCU723 | MW-89 | TLP | 64 | 87 | South Shields County Borough FB | Kepple St-South Shields-1974 <br> K  South Shields-1985-Tyne & Wear MFB/Reserve-1987 |
| AET1C | MW-90 | TL | 64 | 82 | Rotherham County Borough Fire Brigade | Erskine Rd-Rotherham-1974/ D1 Erskine Rd-Rotherham-1982    South Yorkshire County FS |

| | | | | | | | |
|---|---|---|---|---|---|---|---|
| BFJ777B | MW-91 | TL | 64 | 81 | City of Exeter | Howell Rd-Exeter-1974 /E32 Exeter-Devon FB-1981 **Ladder Re-ch onto S&D WY/G&T Power-NTA750W** |
| CYE243C | 43TLP/TL26P MW-92 | TLP | 64 | 86 | LCC London Fire Brigade | A10 Old Court-Kensington-1965 /A28-Kensington-1981 C24 Commercial Rd-Whitechapel-1983/ Reserve-1986 |
| CYE244C | 44TLP/TL27P MW-93 | TLP | 64 | 83 | LCC London Fire Brigade | A4 Euston Rd-Euston-1965 A23 Euston-1981/Reserve-1983 |
| CYE245C | 45TLP/TL28P MW-94 | TLP | 64 | 86 | LCC London Fire Brigade | C26 Milton Court-Barbican-1977 Reserve-1986 |
| CYE246C | 46TLP/TL29P MW-95 | TLP | 64 | 86 | LCC London Fire Brigade | B23-Kingsland Rd-Kingsland-1981 Reserve-1986 |
| CYE247C | 47TLP/TL30P MW-96 | TLP | 64 | 83 | LCC London Fire Brigade | B22 Albert Embankment-Lambeth-1983 **Sold to Universal Cleaners Ltd-Worcestershire** |
| HNO247B | MW-97 | TLP | 64 | | Essex County Fire Brigade | B27/C52 Broadmayne-Basildon **Preserved by Essex County Fire & Rescue Service** |
| JEV57C | MW-98 | TLP | 64 | 85 | Essex County Fire Brigade | A9/A12 St Johns Rd-Clacton **Ladder Re-ch onto Dennis DF133/G&T Power-D886POO** |
| EWR750C | MW-99 | TLP | 64 | 85 | West Riding of Yorkshire FB | Stansfield Rd-Todmorden-1974 /B19 Todmorden-1982 West Yorkshire FS/Reserve-1985 |
| EWR749C | MW-100 | TLP | 64 | ? | West Riding of Yorkshire FB | B14 Stanhope St-Goole-1968 Larsen Rd-Goole-1974 /D2 Goole -1976 D1 Laneham St-Scunthorpe-1984/Humberside FB |
| FGG394C | | TL | 64 | 83 | Glasgow Fire Service (Scotland) | C3 Beith St-Partick-1973 / B5 Alison St-Queens Park-1975 B5-Queens Park-1980-Strathclyde FB Reserve-1983 **Dennis-Metz-100'L** |
| FYS84C | | TL | 64 | 82 | Glasgow Fire Service (Scotland) | C1 Kelbourne St-North West-1965/ A1 Ingram St-Central-1968 A5 Springburn Rd-Springburn-1975 /A3 Springburn-1978 Strathclyde FB Reserve-1982 **Dennis-Metz-100'L** |
| BFL785C EEW693C | MW-101 | TLP | 64 | 84 | Huntingdonshire & Peterborough County Borough FB | ND-14 Dogsthorpe Rd-Peterborough-1974 A14-Peterborough-Cambridgeshire Fire & Rescue |
| CTA297C | MW-102 | TLP | 64 | 81 | Devon Fire Brigade | Newton Rd-Torquay-1974 SD 17 Newton Rd-Torquay-Devon FB **Ladders Re-ch onto S&D WY/G&T Power VDV143X** |
| DKD930C | 1049 MW-103 | TL | 64 | 86 | City of Liverpool | 10 Conleach Rd-Liverpool-1969 9 Longmoor Lane-Fazakerley- Liverpool-1974 N2 Longmoor Lane-Merseyside FB-1984/Reserve-1986 |
| BKY999C | MW-104 | TLP | 64 | 85 | City of Bradford | Nelson St-1974 /A11 Nelson St-1982 **Named 'Harry Smith'** A17 Bradford Rd-Keighley-1985/West Yorkshire FS |
| CRT792C | MW-105 | TLP | 64 | 88 | Suffolk & Ipswich Fire Brigade | Princes St-Ipswich-1974 A2 Princes St-Ipswich-Suffolk FS |
| EYX248C | 48TLP/TL31P MW-107 | TLP | 64 | 86 | GLC London Fire Brigade | H31 Old Town-Croydon-1983 Reserve-1986/**Preserved** |
| ETV999C | MW-108 | TLP | 65 | 83 | City of Nottingham | #1 Shakespeare St-Nottingham-1974 B18 Shakespeare St-Nottingham-Nottinghamshire FB-1983 |
| FBN330D | MW-109 | TLP | 65 | 75 | Bolton County Borough FB | 1 Marsden Rd-Bolton-1970 /1 Moor Lane-Bolton-1974 B20 Moor Lane-Bolton Greater Manchester FS/**Preserved** |
| DEF420D | 10 MW-110 | TLP | 65 | 84 | West Hartlepool County Borough FB | Stranton-West Hartlepool-1974 9 Stranton-Cleveland County FB-1984 Reserve-1984 **Sold Cork County FB-Ireland** |
| JUL57D | TL32P MW-115 | TLP | 65 | 86 | GLC London Fire Brigade | G25 West End Lane-West Hampstead -1972 A21 Harrow Rd-Paddington-1981 Reserve-1986 **Sold to Contractor-Galway-Irish Republic** |
| JUL58D | TL33P MW-113 | TLP | 65 | 86 | GLC London Fire Brigade | G30 Harrow Rd-Wembley-1981 B31 Norwood Rd-West Norwood-1983 Reserve-1986 **Preserved** |
| JUL59D | TL34P MW-114 | TLP | 65 | 78 | GLC London Fire Brigade | A22 Chiltern St-Manchester Square-1977 **Destroyed in a wall collapse-The Granary/Barbican** |

| | | | | | | | |
|---|---|---|---|---|---|---|---|
| JUL60D | TL35P MW-117 | TLP | 65 | 86 | GLC London Fire Brigade | L25 Rainham Rd--Dagenham-1981 Training School-1985 Reserve-1986 |
| JUL61D | TL36P MW-118 | TLP | 65 | 86 | GLC London Fire Brigade | K31 Richmond Rd-Kingston-1983 Reserve-1986 |
| JUL62D | TL37P MW-116 | TLP | 65 | 86 | GLC London Fire Brigade | H21 Old Town-Clapham-1983 Reserve-1986 |
| LWB99D | MW-119 | TLP | 65 | 82 | City of Sheffield | #1 Division St-Sheffield-1974 C1 Division St-Sheffield-1982 /South Yorkshire County FS |
| CFT801D | 146 MW-120 | TLP | 65 | 88 | Tynemouth County Borough FB | Preston Rd North-Tynmouth-1974 /J Tynmouth-1975 Y Dryden Rd-Gateshead-1977 Reserve-1988 Tyne & Wear MFB **Preserved** |
| JVK526D | MW-123 | TL | 65 | 87 | Newcastle & Gateshead Fire Brigade | A1 Pilgrim St-Newcastle Central-1974 D Newcastle Central-1984 /Reserve-1987 Tyne & Wear MFB **Preserved near Ledbury H&W** |
| FCB233D | 1/266 MW-124 | TLP | 65 | 83 | Blackburn County Borough FB | D71 Byrom Rd-Blackburn-1974 B71 Byrom Rd-Blackburn-1983 Lancashire County FB **Preserved** |
| NWY490E | MW-125 | TLP | 65 | 85 | West Riding of Yorkshire FB | A11 Skipton Rd-Harrogate-1974 A1 Harrogate-1983/Reserve-1985 /North Yorkshire FB |
| NWY491E | MW-126 | TLP | 65 | 87 | West Riding of Yorkshire FB | Hightown Rd-Cleckheaton-1974 C13 Cleckheaton-1984 /West Yorkshire FS/ **Preserved** |
| DHC222E | MW-127 | TLP | 65 | 88 | Eastbourne County Borough FB | Whitley Rd-Eastbourne-1974 BD 11 Whitley Rd-East Sussex FB |
| FNH99E | MW-128 | TL | 66 | 86 | Northampton County Borough FB | The Mounts-Northampton-1977 B9 Moulton Way-Moulton-Northampton-1984 B1 The Mounts-Northampton-1986 |
| 383TZ | MW-129 | TLP | 66 | 83 | Belfast Fire Brigade (Northern Ireland) | A2 Bankmore St-Central-1975 A2 Central-Northern Ireland FB-1983 100'L **Ladders Re-ch S&Drewry WY/G&T Power-VIA5732** |

| | | | | | **AEC MERCURY TGM Turntable Ladders** | **The TGM chassis was used to mount the 4 section Merryweather ladder as a replacement for the earlier Mercury chassis. It was fitted with the Ergomatic tilt cab.** |
|---|---|---|---|---|---|---|
| GSP741E | MW-133 | TL | 66 | 89 | Fife Fire Brigade (Scotland) | Carnegie Rd-Dunfermline-Fife Fire Brigade/100'L |
| PAE999F | MW-134 | TLP | 68 | 84 | City of Bristol | #1 Bridewell St-Bristol-1973 #3 St Andrews Rd-Avonmouth-1974 A03 St Andrews Rd-Avonmouth-1984 County of Avon FB/100'L/**Preserved** |
| JFV565F | 250 MW-135 | TL | 66 | 81 | Blackpool County Borough FB | Redbank Rd-Bispham-Blackpool-1974 A31 Bispham-1977 /A37 St Annes Rd-South Shore-1981 Lancashire County FB |
| LBO100F | MW-136 | TLP | 66 | 85 | City of Cardiff (Wales) | Westgate St-Cardiff-1973 /Adam St-Cardiff-1974 1 Adam St-South Glamorgan FS-1985/100/**Preserved** |
| EGL678F | MW-137 | TLP | 66 | 86 | City of Bath | Cleveland Bridge-City of Bath-1974 B1 Cleveland Bridge-Bath-1986/County of Avon FB /100'L **Sold to K. Lloyd Tree Surgeon-Colwall nr Ledbury H&W** |
| MLV605F | MW-138 | TL | 66 | 85 | City of Liverpool | 12 Studholme St-Bankhall-1973 12 West Derby Rd-Liverpool-1974 /C4 West Derby Rd-1985 Merseyside FB/100'L/**Preserved** |
| MLV606F | MW-139 | TL | 66 | 81 | City of Liverpool | 9 Longmoor Lane-Fazakerly-1974 N1 Longmoor Lane-1985/Merseyside FB/100'L |
| EJC870F | MW-140 | TLP | 66 | 84 | Caernarvonshire FB (Wales) | Beach Rd-Bangor-CFB-1974 01 Beach Rd-Bangor-1984 /Gwynedd FB/100'L |
| MAJ921F | MW-144 | TLP | 67 | 88 | North Riding of Yorkshire FB | B1 North Marine Drive-Scarborough-1974 ED 1 North Marine Drive-Scarborough North Yorkshire FB/100'L |

| | | | | | | |
|---|---|---|---|---|---|---|
| GDY99F | MW-146 | TLP | 67 | 90 | Hastings County Borough FB | Bohemia Rd-Hastings-1974 /B8 Bohemia Rd-Hastings East Sussex FB/100'L/**Preserved** |
| ULR67F | MW-147 | TLP | 67 | 89 | Fire Service College Moreton in Marsh Gloucestershire | FSC Moreton in Marsh-Gloucestershire/100'L **Involved in fatal collapse in Cornwall .**Resulted in all Merryweather Re-chassied appliances being checked and where necessary withdrawn. |
| ULR68F | MW-148 | TLP | 67 | 88 | Fire Service College Moreton in Marsh Gloucestershire | FSC Moreton in Marsh-Gloucestershire/100'L |
| MMR217G | MW-149 | TLP | 68 | 94 | Wiltshire Fire Brigade | 3/1 Ashley Rd-Sailsbury-1990 /Reserve-1994 Wiltshire FB/100'L |
| ARB995G | MW-153 | TL | 68 | 88 | Derbyshire Fire Service | C1 Sheffield Rd-Chesterfield-Derbyshire/100'L |
| CFK291G | MW-154 | TL | 68 | 91 | Worcester City & County FB | Copenhagen St-Worcester-1974 21 Copenhagen St-Worcester-1991/Hereford & Worcester FB 100'L/**Sold to a Liverpool Docks Works FB** |
| BWU290H | MW-158 | TL | 68 | 90 | West Riding of Yorkshire FB | Bradford Rd-Keighley-1974 A17-Bradford Rd-Keighley-1990/West Yorkshire FS/100'L **Sold to Butler Guinness, Ireland /Preserved** |
| TUX198J | MW-163 | TL | 69 | 91 | Shropshire Fire Service | St Michael's St-Shrewsbury Shropshire FS/100'L |
| PPR812K | MW-166 | TLP | 70 | 88 | Dorset Fire Brigade | B18 Wimborne Rd-Poole-1986 B23 Almhurst Rd-Westbourne-1988 /100'L **Sold to Tree Surgeon in the Nottingham area.** |
| PPR813K | MW-167 | TLP | 70 | 90 | Dorset Fire Brigade | A07 North Quay-Weymouth-1990 Reserve-Dorset FB 100'L |
| 6524ZE | MW-168 | TL | 70 | ? | Dublin Fire Brigade (Irish Republic) | |

| | | | | | AEC MERCURY Hydraulic Platforms | |
|---|---|---|---|---|---|---|
| 513BGE | | HPP | 60 | 80 | Glasgow Fire Service (Scotland) | ex TL / A3 Cuthelton St-Parkhead JC Bennett-Simon SS65-**Booms mounted in 1968 Booms Re-ch onto S& Drewry WY-OYS620V** |
| 209HAT | | PHP | 64 | 84 | City of Kingston upon Hull | B1 Southgates Lane-Hull East-1974 B2 Noodle Hill Way-Bransholme-Humberside FB-1984 HCB Angus-Simon SS65/**Booms removed and preserved** |
| BAD659B | | PHP | 64 | 75 | Gloucestershire Fire Service | 12 Keynsham Rd-Cheltenham-1967 Rodway Rd-Patchway-1969 /Tenniscourt Rd-Kingswood-1974 B7 Kingswood-1975 /County of Avon HCB-Simon SS65 |
| CBE173C | | PHP | 65 | 90 | Lindsey County FB (Lincolnshire) | Churchill Ave-Skegness-1974 C1 Skegness-1990 /Lincolnshire Fire Brigade HCB Angus-Simon SS65 |
| LNM887G | | PHP | 68 | 83 | Bedfordshire Fire Service | 02 Barkers Lane-Bedford-1972 02 Brewers Hill Rd-Dunstable-1983 **Sold to Cork County FB-Mallow-Re-registered-792PZB** TGM-Ergomatic-Merryweather-SS50 |
| RGD999G | | HP | 68 | 90 | Glasgow Fire Service (Scotland) | C1-Kelbourne St-North West-1975 A04 Kelbourne St-North West-1985/Training School-1990 Strathclyde Fire Brigade TGM-Ergomatic-JC Bennett-SS70 |
| 1832WZ | | HP | 68 | 82 | City of Belfast (Northern Ireland) | A06 Upper Newtownards Rd-Knock-Belfast-1973 A06 Knock-Northern Ireland FB-1982 **Preserved** TGM-Ergomatic-Carmichael Orbitor-72' |
| NAV853H | | HP | 70 | 89 | North Eastern Area FB (Scotland) | King St-Aberdeen-1975 /S96 King St-Aberdeen-1982 S97 Souterhead Rd-Altens-Aberdeen-1989 Grampian Fire Brigade **Sold toKildare County FB-Maynooth-Re-reg-70KE2** TGM-Ergomatic-JC Bennett SS70 |

16

| | | | | | | |
|---|---|---|---|---|---|---|
| YNM439L | | PHP | 72 | 82 | Bedfordshire Fire Service | 01 Barkers Lane-Bedford-1982<br>**Sold to Cork County FB-Cobh /Re-registered-791PZB**<br>TGM Ergomatic-Merryweather SS50 |
| VET3L | | PHP | 72 | 84 | Rotherham County Borough<br>Fire Brigade | Erskine Rd-Rotherham-1974<br>D1 Rotherham-South Yorkshire CFB-1984 /**Preserved**<br>TGM-Ergomatic-Merryweather SS50 |

Only four Simon hydraulic booms were mounted on the early AEC Mercury chassis. Delivered to Cheltenham in 1964, BAD659B was transfered to Kingswood in 1967 which was then part of Gloucestershire though in 1974 passed to the County of Avon Fire Brigade. The others were found at Skegness, Hull East and Glasgow.
*Keith Wardell collection*

YNM439L is an AEC TGM chassied pump hydraulic platform and was delivered to the Bedfordshire Fire Service in 1972. It served at the Barkers Lane station in Bedford for 10 years, quite a short period for an aerial appliance, and passed to Cork County fire service in the Irish Republic. *Mike Bunn*

**Pictured here is 4919RH. This superb looking AEC Mercury/Merryweather appliance is most enthusiast's image of the 1960s big city Emergency Tender. It was originally delivered as a Foam Tender/Carrier, but took on the ET role in 1972. It served the Hull area for nearly 22 years from 1963, proving that 'They really built 'em in those days'. The photograph was taken outside Hull North fire station, which was part of the City of Kingston Fire Brigade until 1974 when it passed to the Humberside Fire Brigade.** *Steve Shaw*

| | | | | | AEC Chassied Emergency/Rescue Tenders | The Regent 111 bus chassis proved the ideal platform for the early ET's and special appliances, later replaced by the Mercury lorry chassis. The Regent was powered by the 9.6 litre Meadows petrol engine, while the Mercury had an AEC AV470 diesel unit. |
|---|---|---|---|---|---|---|
| OXT779 | ET6A | ET | 54 | 75 | LCC London Fire Brigade | D61 Albert Embankment-Lambeth-1959 C21 Old St-Shoreditch-1970 /Reserve-1975/**Preserved** Regent 111-Park Royal |
| 999DRB | | ET | 57 | 81 | Derbyshire Fire Service | Sheffield Rd-Chesterfield-1974 /C1 Chesterfield-1981 Marquis-Merryweather |
| NJD999 | ET10 | ET | 59 | 76 | West Ham County Borough FB | Prince Regent Lane-Plaistow- West Ham-1965 L21 High St-East Ham-1976 Reserve-1976 /London FB Mercury-Merryweather |
| XJB999 | | ET/CU | 61 | 77 | Reading & Berkshire Fire Brigade | W3 Dee Road-Reading-1970 W2 Wokingham Rd-Reading-1974/W2 Wokingham Rd-1977 Royal Berkshire Fire Brigade-**Officially Termed Special Unit** Mercury-Carmichael |
| GCU377 | | ET/CU | 62 | 82 | South Shields County Borough FB | Kepple St-South Shields-1974 ED K Kepple St-South Shields-1982 Tyne & Wear MFB Marquis-Merryweather |
| 3982RU | | ET | 63 | 81 | Bournemouth County Borough FB | Holdenhurst Rd-Bournemouth-1974 B24 Holdenhurst Rd-1981-Dorset Fire Brigade Mercury-HCB |
| 4919RH | | FoT ET | 63 | 83 | City of Kingston upon Hull FB | #1 Worship St-Hull Central-1969 #4 Clough Rd-Hull North-1974 A02 Clough Rd-Hull North-1983 -Humberside Fire Brigade Mercury-Merryweather |
| 4999SC | | ET | 63 | 85 | South Eastern Area Fire Brigade (Scotland) | Lauriston Place Edingburgh-South Eastern AFB-1975 50 Lauriston Place Edingburgh-1985 Lothian & Borders FB Mercury-Merryweather |
| 867HGB | | ET | 63 | 80 | Glasgow Fire Service (Scotland) | B1 South-Glasgow-1974 B1 South-Glasgow- 1980/Strathclyde Fire Brigade Mercury-Carmichael |
| AYS273B | | ET | 64 | 76 | Glasgow Fire Service (Scotland) | A1 Ingram St-Central-Glasgow-1975 **Converted Breathing Apparatus Tender**/Strathclyde FB Mercury-Carmichael |
| ERA897C | | ET | 65 | 84 | Derbyshire Fire Service | A1 Derby Rd-Ilkeston Mercury Merryweather |

The coupling of an AEC Mercury chassis with Carmichael bodywork for an emergency tender/control unit was rare though one example, XJB999, is seen here and was originally termed a 'Special Unit'. This example served at the Wokingham and Dee Road stations in Reading, Berkshire. The two others of this type were based at Glasgow and Belfast.
*Keith Wardell collection*

19

| | | | | | | |
|---|---|---|---|---|---|---|
| HBC945D | No-8 | ET/CU | 66 | 83 | City of Leicester | Lancaster Rd-Leicester-1974 /SD 30 Leicester Central-1985 **Converted Emergency Rescue Tender** Leicestershire Fire Brigade/**Preserved** Mercury-Merryweather |
| KDF146E | | Res/T | 67 | 82 | Gloucestershire Fire Service | 07 Pagenhill Lane-Stroud /**Preserved** **Dial Holmes '750' twin boom wrecker, capacity of each boom 4 tonnes extended, 12 tonnes retracted, telescopic flood light mast. Sold to a garage in the Devon area.** TGM-6 Mercury-Marshall |
| LTV999F | | WRT CRT | 67 | 88 | City of Nottingham | B20 Stockhill Lane-Nottingham-1974 B20 Stockhill-1988/**Winch Fitted** /Nottinghamshire FB TGM 7 Mercury-HCB Angus |
| NWJ578K | | ET | 72 | 85 | City of Sheffield | Division St-Sheffield-City of Sheffield FB-1974 C1 Division St-Sheffield-1985-South Yorkshire CFB **Preserved/Terra Search Crane/Sold to a Hampshire Garage** TGM-7 Mercury-HCB Angus |
| EOI5678 | | ET | 73 | 87 | Belfast Fire Brigade (Northern Ireland) | Bankmore St-Central-Belfast-1973/A02 Central-Belfast-1985 FBReserve-1987-Northern Ireland TGM-7 Mercury-Carmichael |

| | | | | | | |
|---|---|---|---|---|---|---|
| | | | | | **AEC Chassied Specials** | The Mercury chassis which dated from 1953 was a popular chassis for most of the appliances featured below. It had a payload of 10 ton and was powered on the most part by the AEC AV470 diesel engine. |
| NKG91 | | PMover | 55 | 78 | City of Cardiff (Wales) | **ex Pump 03 Crowbridge** #1 Westgate St-Central Cardiff-1973 #1 Adam St-Central Cardiff-1974 1 Adam St-Central Cardiff-1978 South Glamorgan FS Mercury-Merryweather/SGFB |
| TGU711 | | WRC | 57 | 78 | Bedfordshire Fire Service | 2 Brewers Hill Rd-Dunstable Mercury-Sun Engineering |
| TGU713 | | WRC | 57 | 78 | Bedfordshire Fire Service | 1 Barkers Lane-Bedford-1974 12 Southfields Rd-Kempston-1978 Mercury-Sun Engineering |
| 6399KH | | C/Unit | 59 | 81 | City of Kingston upon Hull Fire Brigade | #1 Worship St-Hull Central-1974 A1 Worship St-Hull Central-1981 /Humberside Fire Brigade Merryweather-Marquis |
| RJD344 | FT.3 | FOT | 60 | 78 | West Ham County Borough Fire Brigade | Romford Rd-Stratford-1965 F21 Romford Rd-Stratford-1972 J21 Church St-Edmonton-1978 /London Fire Brigade Mercury-Merryweather |
| AYS273B | | BAT | 64 | ? | Glasgow Fire Service (Scotland) | **ex ET A1 Ingram St-Glasgow-1974** A1 Ingram St-Glasgow-1975 A1 Ingram St-Glasgow- Strathclyde Fire Brigade Mercury-Carmichael |
| FGG121C | | FOT | 65 | ? | Glasgow Fire Service (Scotland) | B1 South Fire Station-Glasgow-1975 B1 South Fire Station-Glasgow-1980 D3 Pennyburn-Irvine North-Strathclyde Fire Brigade Mercury-Pyrene |
| FYS879C | | FOT | 65 | ? | Glasgow Fire Service (Scotland) | C1 Kelbourne St-North West-Glasgow-1975 A4 Kelbourne St-North West-Strathclyde Fire Brigade Mercury-Pyrene |
| DCU14D | | FOT | 66 | 84 | South Shields County Borough Fire Brigade | Kepple St-South Shields-1974 V Dryden Rd-Gateshead-1984 /Tyne & Wear Metropolitan FB Mercury-Merryweather |
| KGA86D | | Rec/V | 66 | ? | Glasgow Fire Service (Scotland) | Brigade Workshops Matador-Bates Holmes |
| ULR69F | | Rec/V | 67 | | Fire Service College | **ex Pump Escape** Moreton in Marsh-Gloucestershire Mercury TGM-Merryweather/FSC |

Gloucestershire ran three heavy rescue appliances, one of which, KDF146E, a 1967 AEC Mercury TGM with Bates Holmes crane, ran from Pagen Hill station in Stroud. The other, a Ford D Series also with Bates Holmes crane, operated out of Cheltenham where it replaced the earlier Bedford-chassied example. The Dial Holmes twin booms have a lifting capacity of 12 tonnes when retracted. *Michael Lawmon*

| NDC646G | 24 | FOT | 68 | 80 | Tees-side Fire Brigade | 2 South Rd-Norton-1972 /7 Carew Rd-Billingham-1974 7 Seaton Carew Rd-Billingham-1980 **Written off in RTA/**Cleveland County Fire Brigade Mercury TGM-Merryweather |
|---|---|---|---|---|---|---|
| KWW227K | | WRC | 71 | 84 | West Riding of Yorkshire Fire Brigade | South Lane-Elland-1974 B13 South Lane-Elland- West Yorkshire Fire Service Mercury TGM-Carmichael |
| KWW228K | | WRC | 71 | 84 | West Riding of Yorkshire Fire Brigade | Dale St-Ossett-1974 F17 Dale St-Ossett- West Yorkshire Fire Service Mercury TGM-Carmichael |
| CDC341K | 27 | FOT | 71 | 92 | Tees-side Fire Brigade | Middlesbrough Rd East-Middlesbrough-1974 3 South Loop Rd-Grangetown-1987/Reserve-1991 Cleveland County Fire Brigade Mercury TGM-Carmichael |

# ALBION

| Reg No | Fleet No | TYPE | YR | OS | Appliance & Brigade Name | Details/Stations |
|--------|----------|------|----|----|--------------------------|------------------|
| | | | | | **Albion Chassied Specialist Appliances Weight** AZ/1.5 Tons FT/4 to 5 Tons CX/6.5 to 14.5 Tons Chieftain/6 Tons upwards Claymore/Clydesdale/4 to 5 Tons | **The Albion chassis range was rarely used for Fire Appliances. The early specials were mounted on the CX chassis. The later models were mounted on a variety of chassis types. The engines were normally of the Leyland diesel variety. In 1972 Albion became part of Leyland Motors.** |
| CGE756 | | ET | 36 | ? | Glasgow Fire Service (Scotland) | CX14-Merryweather |
| FGU694 | ET4 | ET | 37 | 61 | LCC London Fire Brigade | A1-Lambeth /D61 Albert Embankment-Lambeth 1961 CX14-Merryweather |
| 342EYR | | WRC | 63 | 79 | Worcester City & County Fire Brigade | Windsor St-Bromsgrove-1974/25 Windsor St-Bromsgrove-1979 Hereford & Worcester FB-**ex Petrol Tanker** Reiver- |
| 6330VR | | Salv/T | 63 | 77 | City of Manchester | Rochdale Rd-Blackley/E51 Blackley-Greater Manchester Claymore-Cocker |
| AVM3B | | Salv/T | 64 | 75 | City of Manchester | London Rd-Manchester Claymore-Cocker |
| ANF720B | | FOT | 64 | ? | City of Manchester | London Rd-1967 /Briscoe Lane-Philips Park-1974 E52 Philips Park-Greater Manchester 1979 Chieftain-Pyrene |
| CCP343C | | PHP ET | 65 | 88 | Halifax County Borough FB | Skircoat Moor Rd-Halifax-1974 A11-Nelson St-Bradford-1987/Reserve-1988 West Yorkshire FS Chieftain-Carmichael-Simon-**DS50** |
| LDJ999E | | ET | 67 | 83 | St Helens County Borough FB | Parr Stocks Rd-St Helens-1974 E1 St Helens-Merseyside FB-1983 Albion Chieftain-Carmichael |
| EHD38F | | ET | 67 | 83 | Dewsbury County Borough FB | Huddersfield Rd-Dewsbury C14-Dewsbury-1983/West Yorkshire FS Chieftain-Carmichael |

| | NFS Merryweather Ladder No-MW | | | | **Albion Chassied Turntable Ladders** | **Albion appliances were supplied with either a 4 or 6 cylinder engine.** |
|--------|-------------------------------|------|----|----|----------------------------------------|---------------------------------------------------------------------------|
| FJ3874 | | TL | ? | 42 | City of Exeter | Howells Rd-Exeter Merryweather-85 Wooden Ladder |
| RY5790 | 9 | TLP | 27 | 42 | City of Leicester Fire Brigade | Lancaster Rd-Leicester Merryweather-85 **Wooden Ladder-300gpm P** |
| SC5676 | MW-2 | TL | 28 | ? | Edinburgh Fire Brigade | Lauriston Place-Edinburgh Merryweather-90/95 L Wooden |
| KR3993 | MW-3 | TLP | 30 | ? | Kent Fire Brigade | **King St-Margate- ? / Market Place-Deal- ?** Merryweather- 85 L Wooden-**350gpmP** |
| DR7555 | | TL | 32 | 42 | City of Plymouth | ? Merryweather-85 L Wooden |
| MAN875 | | TLP | 33 | 62 | Isle of Man Fire Brigade | Douglas Fire Station Merryweather-100'L |
| CPE218 | MW-13 | TL | 35 | 49 | Wimbledon Fire Brigade | Kingston St-Wimbledon-1949-**Preserved in Surrey** Merryweather-70'L |
| FPL14 | MW-25 | TLP | 37 | 61 | Merton & Morden FB (Surrey) | Richmond Rd-Kingston-1948 Richmond Rd-Kingston-1950 / Reserve-1961 / Surrey CCFB Merryweather-75'L-**250gpmP** |

The Albion Chieftain chassis was only used once to mount hydraulic platform booms. CCP343C is the unique appliance which served Halifax County Borough and West Yorkshire for 23-years. It was delivered in 1965 as a Pump Hydraulic Platform/Emergency Tender which, in itself, is a very rare combination. The photograph shows it in its later years in West Yorkshire livery. *Steve Shaw*

# BMC

| Reg No | Fleet No | TYPE | YR | OS | Appliance & Brigade Name | Details/Stations |
|---|---|---|---|---|---|---|
| Chassis<br>FG<br>FJ<br>FK<br>LD<br>FH<br>Terrier<br>Boxer<br>Mastiff | | | | | Weight<br>1 to 5 Tons<br>up to 18 Tons<br>2 Tons<br>1 to 1.5 Tons<br>7 to 8 Tons<br>6.5 to 9.5 Tons<br>10 to 16 Tons<br>16 to 24 to 28 Tons | In 1952 Austin & Morris Motor Company's amalgamated to become BMC British Motor Corporation. In 1968 it became part of the Leyland Motor's Group and finally disappeared in 1970. The engines in the range varied from the small petrol engines up to Perkins V8's. |
| CDJ57 | | ET | 52 | 67 | St Helens County Borough Fire Brigade | #1Parade St-St Helens-1959/#1 Parr Stocks Rd-St Helens-1967    Morris FFK- |
| PED555 | | Res/T | 55 | 69 | Warrington County Borough Fire Brigade | Heathside-Warrington-1968/Winwick St-Warrington-1969 Austin FFG-Marsden |
| 80JPE | 29 | F/SalvT | 59 | 72 | Surrey County Council Fire Brigade | 29 Church St-Woking Austin FFG-HCB |
| 79GPK | 12 | F/SalvT | 59 | 72 | Surrey County Council Fire Brigade | 12 Spook Hill-Dorking Austin FFG-HCB |
| 7351VX | | AT | 60 | 72 | Essex County Fire Brigade | C51 North Rd-Brentwood Austin LD- |
| RHS520 | | H/Fot | 60 | ? | Western Area Fire Brigade (Scotland) | Canal St-Paisley Austin FFG-HCB |
| VDW644 | | FOT | 60 | 76 | Newport County Borough Fire Service (Wales) | #1 Dock St-Malpas-Newport-1969/#1 Malpas Rd-1974 B9 Malpas Rd-1976/Gwent Fire Brigade LD 30cwt |
| 5704HP | | F/SalvT | 61 | 80 | City of Coventry Fire Brigade | #3 Foleshill Rd-Foleshill-1974 B5 Foleshill-1980 /West Midlands Fire Service Morris FF-Lewis Scott |

Photographed outside the Bryans Lane station in Rugeley is CCH132H, a BMC Boxer Water Carrier. New in 1970 to the Staffordshire Fire Brigade it had a tanker body provided by Butterfield. The capacity of the tank was a 1000 gallons. Staffordshire have always operated Water Carriers and currently operate two 4x4 Bedford TM chassied machines at Cannock and Leek.
*Mike Bunn*

| | | | | | | |
|---|---|---|---|---|---|---|
| **VDO600** | | ET<br>Salv/T | 62 | ? | Holland County Fire Brigade | **Converted to Road Accident Recovery Vehicle**<br>Austin FFG-Carmichael |
| **XDO545** | | Pump/RT<br>Salv/T | 62 | ? | Holland County Fire Brigade | Converted to Road Accident Vehicle<br>Austin FGK-Carmichael |
| **5888HA** | | ET | 62 | 80 | Smethwick County Borough Fire<br>Brigade | #2 Judge St-Oldbury-1974<br>D01 Old Park Lane-Oldbury-1977<br>**Converted Foam Salvage Tender**<br>C8 Brook Lane-Billesley-1980/West Midlands Fire Service<br>Morris FF-Dayson |
| **UHS171** | | H/Fot | 62 | ? | Western Area Fire Brigade<br>(Scotland) | Rue End St-Greenock<br>Austin FFG/HCB |
| **20CDU** | | HLL | 63 | 80 | City of Coventry Fire Brigade | #2 Sir Henry Parkes Rd-Canley-1974<br>B4 Canley-1980/West Midlands Fire Service<br>Morris FF-Lewis Scott |
| **425UFK** | | ET | 63 | 83 | Worcester City & County<br>Fire Brigade | SD1 Copenhagen St-Worcester-1974/21 Worcester-1977<br>**Converted Foam Salvage Tender**<br>21 Worcester-1983 /Hereford & Worcester FB<br>Morris FG-HCB |
| **2360FG** | | Foam/C | 63 | 90 | Fife Fire Brigade<br>(Scotland) | A3 Dunnikeir Rd-Kirkaldy-1964<br>A1 Carnegie Drive-Dunfermline-1983<br>**Converted Decontamination Unit**<br>A1 Carnegie Drive-Dunfermline-1990<br>Morris FFG-HCB |
| **69XFK** | | F/SalvT | 64 | 78 | Worcester City & County<br>Fire Brigade | ND5 Hagley Rd-Halesowen-1974<br>F01 Tower Rd-Dudley-1978/West Midlands Fire Service<br>Morris FG-HCB |
| **ACC537B** | | Res/T | 64 | 74 | Caernarvonshire County FB<br>(Wales) | Beach Rd-Bangor<br>Austin Mastiff |
| **ASP841B** | | E/Salv | 64 | 80 | Fife Fire Brigade<br>(Scotland) | A3 Dunnikeir Rd-Kirkaldy-1980<br>Morris FFG-HCB |
| **ASP842B** | | C/Unit | 64 | 86 | Fife Fire Brigade<br>(Scotland) | A5 Methilhaven Rd-Methil-1980/HQ Thornton-1986<br>Morris FFG-HCB |
| **BPE898B** | | BAT | 64 | 77 | Surrey County Council<br>Fire Brigade | Croydon Rd-Reigate-1977<br>Morris FFG-Wadhams/SCCFB |
| **BPJ15B** | | C/Unit | 64 | 70 | Surrey County Council<br>Fire Brigade | Croydon Rd-Reigate-1970<br>Morris FFG-Wadhams/SCCFB |
| **BGG944B** | | C/Unit | 64 | ? | Glasgow Fire Service<br>(Scotland) | C1 Kelbourne St-North West /Marine Fire Station<br>Austin FFG-Bennett |
| **DGA918B** | | CAV | 64 | ? | Glasgow Fire Service<br>(Scotland) | C1 Kelbourne St-North West /Marine Fire Station<br>Austin LD-Bennett |
| **CJL999C** | | Pump/RT<br>Salv/T | 65 | ? | Holland County Fire Brigade<br>(Lincolnshire) | **Donated Fire Service Museum Trust**<br>Morris FGK-Carmichael |
| **JKD121D** | | Artic/TU | 66 | 81 | City of Liverpool | #1 Hatton Gardens-Liverpool-1969<br>#1 Studholme St-Bankhall-1974<br>C1 Studholme St-Bankhall-1981<br>Merseyside Fire Brigade /**Articulated Unit**<br>Austin FFK240-Taskers |
| **JJW999D** | | Hose<br>F/Salv/T | 66 | 84 | Wolverhampton County Borough<br>Fire Brigade | #2 Bushbury Rd-Fallings Park-1974<br>E6 Fallings Park-1984 /West Midlands Fire Service<br>Morris FFG-Carmichael |
| **DJC202D** | | C/Unit | 66 | ? | Caernarvonshire County FB<br>(Wales) | Beach Rd-Bangor-1973<br>Morris FFG- |
| **DJC203D** | | Salv/T | 66 | ? | Caernarvonshire County FB<br>(Wales) | Beach Rd-Bangor-1973<br>Morris FFG- |
| **ESA597D** | | CAV | 66 | 86 | North Eastern Area Fire Brigade<br>(Scotland) | North Anderson Drive-Aberdeen/Grampian Fire Brigade<br>Austin FFG-Federal Industries |

Photographed outside Copenhagen Street in Worcester was 425UFK, a Morris FG with ET/Salvage Tender bodywork that served Worcester City and County Fire Brigade from 1963 until 1974. It then passed to the Hereford and Worcester Fire Brigade being replaced by a Ford D Series in 1978. It was finally retired in 1983, following an accident that the author attended as a member of Hereford & Worcester Ambulance Service. *Ian Moore*

| | | | | | | |
|---|---|---|---|---|---|---|
| JRM875D | | FOT | 66 | 75 | Cumberland County Fire Brigade | Hensingham-Whitehaven-1974<br>Hensingham-Whitehaven-1975/<br>Cumbria Fire Service-**Written off in RTA**<br>Austin FFG- |
| GJL555E | | Crash Tender | 67 | ? | Holland County Fire Brigade | Spalding Fire Station<br>Morris FFG-Sun |
| NKD162F | | Artic/TU | 67 | 81 | City of Liverpool | #1 Hatton Gardens-Liverpool-1969<br>#1 Studholme St-Bankhall-1974<br>C1 Studholme St-Bankhall-1981<br>Merseyside Fire Brigade /**Articulated Unit**<br>Austin FJK240-Taskers |
| OEA999F | R-168 | CU/ET BAT | 67 | 78 | West Bromwich County Borough | #1 West Bromwich-1973/#1 Hargate Lane-West Brom-1974<br>D8 West Bromwich-1976/D9 Tower St-Dudley-1978<br>West Midlands Fire Service<br>Morris FFG-Benson |
| NGE656F | | Hi-ex Fot | 68 | ? | Glasgow Fire Service (Scotland) | A1 Ingram St-Central<br>Austin LD-Bennett |
| FEF871F | | Foam/C | 68 | 74 | West Hartlepool County Borough FB | Stranton-West Hartlepool-1974<br>Morris FFG- |
| CCH132H | | WRC | 70 | 84 | Staffordshire Fire Brigade | Rugeley Fire Station-1974 / Bryans Lane-Rugeley-1984<br>Boxer-Butterfield |
| CUB904J | | Salv/T | 71 | ? | Leeds City Fire Brigade | Leeds City Fire Stations<br>FG-LCFB |
| RWW290R | | Salv/T | 76 | 88 | West Yorkshire Fire Service | A12 Keighley Rd-Bingley-1982<br>**Converted Damage Prevention Unit**<br>A12 Keighley Rd-Bingley-1988<br>Leyland FG-Anglo |

An unusual-looking Morris FFG with Benson bodywork is OEA999F, seen here at Oldbury in the West Midlands. It was delivered to the former West Bromwich County Borough fire service as an Emergency Tender Control Unit in 1967. It also carried out breathing apparatus duties before passing to West Midlands Fire Service with the amalgamation of the brigades in 1974.
*Les Edkins*

**AWO674K was the first Ford chassis used to mount Simon SS50 hydraulic booms. This Hydraulic Platform was delivered in 1972 to Ebbw Vale in Monmouthshire passing to Gwent Fire Brigade in 1974. It was sold in 1987 to Hoistline, a company in the Isle of Man, and many Fire Brigade Society members saw it on the AGM visit there in 1992**. *David Thomas*

# FORD

| Reg No | Fleet No | TYPE | YR | OS | BRIGADE | Details/Stations |
|--------|----------|------|----|----|---------|------------------|
| | | | | | **Ford Chassied Aerial Appliances** | **Most of the Aerials were mounted on the heavier (16 ton) D1617 chassis.** |
| AWO674K | | PHP | 72 | 87 | Monmouthshire County Council Fire Brigade (Wales) | Cemetery Rd-Ebbw Vale-1974/C5 Ebbw Vale-1981 C01 Darren Drive-Abercarn-1987 **Sold to Hoistline- Isle of Man-Re-reg CMN999A** D1014-HCB Angus-Simon SS50 |
| DRM620K | | PHP | 72 | 90 | Cumberland Fire Brigade | AD King St-Workington-1990 D1617-HCB Angus-Simon SS50 |
| UTE950L | 186 | PHP | 72 | 87 | Lancashire County Fire Brigade | A12 Clarke St-Morecambe-1982 A32 Radcliffe Rd-Fleetwood-1987 D1617-HCB Angus-Simon SS50 |
| WTF85L | 188 | HP | 72 | 90 | Lancashire County Fire Brigade | D70 Manchester Rd-Accrington-1974 /B70 Accrington-1990 D1617-HCB Angus-Simon SS85 |
| LVT462P | | HP | 76 | 94 | Staffordshire Fire Brigade | ND Lower Bethesda St-Hanley-1988 SD Lammascote Rd-Stafford-1994/**Sold to Angloco's Batley** D1617-Evans-Simon SS263 |
| WUY322R | | HP | 77 | 93 | Hereford & Worcester Fire Brigade | ND 27 Birmingham Rd-Redditch-1993 **Booms Re-chassied onto Volvo FL7-Angloco-L301UWP** D1617-Carmichael-Simon SS263 |
| YPA829T | | HP | 78 | 96 | Surrey County Council Fire Brigade | WD 22 By Pass Ladymead-Guilford D1617-Cheshire FE-Simon SS263 |
| YPA130T | | HP | 78 | 96 | Surrey County Council Fire Brigade | ED 13 Cobham Rd-Leatherhead D1617-Cheshire FE-Simon SS263 |
| YJM102T | S9 | TL | 78 | 87 | Royal Berkshire & Reading Fire Brigade | E18 London Rd-Langley-1983/E13 St Marks Rd-Windsor-1987 **Ladders Re-chassied off Commer QX-Haydon-792TKX Buckinghamshire FB** D1114-Carmichael-Magirus DL30 |
| CHB660V | | HP | 80 | 92 | Gwent Fire Brigade | B20 Henllys Way-Cwmbran-1992 D1617-Cheshire FE-Simon SS70 |
| KPF814W | | HP | 80 | 96 | Surrey County Council Fire Brigade | ND 33 Addlestone Moor-Chertsey D1617-Cheshire FE-Simon SS263 |
| EBP334W | S10 | TL | 81 | 92 | Royal Berkshire & Reading Fire Brigade | 01 Caversham Rd-Reading-1983 17 Tuns Lane-Slough-1989/Reserve-1992 **Ladders Re-ch off AEC Mercury-Haydon-RDH909 Walsall County Borough FB** D1617-Carmichael-Magirus DL30 |
| TIA1099 | | HP | 82 | | Northern Ireland Fire Brigade | A06 Upper Newtownards Rd-Knock-Belfast-1989/Reserve- **Originally ordered for Staffordshire Fire Brigade** D1617-Cheshire FE-Simon SS263 |
| | | | | | **Ford Chassied Emergency/Rescue Tenders** | |
| **Chassis** Thames Thames Van Trader D Series Cargo-Iveco | | | 39 55 57 65 81 | 57 65 65 81 | **Weight/Engine** 2 to 3 Tons /3.6 litre diesel 10/12cwt-15 cwt/Consul/Zephyr 2 to 8 Tons/4.8-5.4 litre diesel 4 to 10 Tons 6 to 28 Tons | **The Ford range of specials have had a variety of engine sizes from the small 1.6 petrol engines through to the Ford 6 litre in the D Series. The early Fordson appliances are covered in another listing. In 1986 the Commercial vehicles Division was taken over by Iveco (Industrial Vehicles Corporation) the commercial wing of FIAT.** |
| 9999JW | 219 | ET | 62 | 76 | Wolverhampton County Borough Fire Brigade | Fallings Park-1974 / E1 Blue Lane West-Walsall-1978 Reserve-1982 -West Midlands Fire Service Thames-Miles-Anglo |
| 288RFC | | ET | 63 | 78 | City of Oxford Fire Brigade | Rewley Rd-Oxford-1974 B01 Rewley Rd-Oxford-Oxfordshire Fire Service Thames Trader-HCB |

| | | | | | | |
|---|---|---|---|---|---|---|
| OTN703F | 212 | E/ST | 68 | 82 | Newcastle & Gateshead Joint Fire Service | B1 Dryden Rd-Gateshead-1974 **Stores Van-1982**/Tyne & Wear Metropolitan FB D600-Killingworth Koachworks |
| TCM167L | 1124 | Res/T | 72 | 83 | Birkenhead County Borough Fire Brigade | Whetstone Lane-Birkenhead-1974 W1 Exmouth St-Birkenhead-1983 Merseyside Fire Brigade D800-HCB Angus |
| XBL433L | 20 | ET | 72 | 92 | City of Portsmouth Fire Brigade | #3 Waytes Rd-Cosham-Portsmouth 1974 B23 Cosham-1978 B24 Somers Rd-Southsea-Portsmouth-1992/Hampshire FB D1014-HCB Angus |
| GDG559N | | ERA | 74 | 84 | Gloucestershire Fire Service | 12 Keynsham Rd-Cheltenham-1984 **Front mounted winch-Lighting mast** **Dial Holmes '750' twin boom wrecker capacity of each boom-4 tonnes extended-12 tonnes retracted.** DT2417-Bates Holmes |
| KNP439T | 219 | Res/T | 78 | 90 | Hereford & Worcester Fire Brigade | 21 Copenhagen St-Worcester-1990 **Originally supplied with rotating Breathing Apparatus loading Mechanism** D1114-Cheshire FE |
| JEH541V | | ET | 80 | 87 | Staffordshire Fire Brigade | SD Lammascote Rd-Stafford-1987/**Written off in RTA** D1114-Benson |

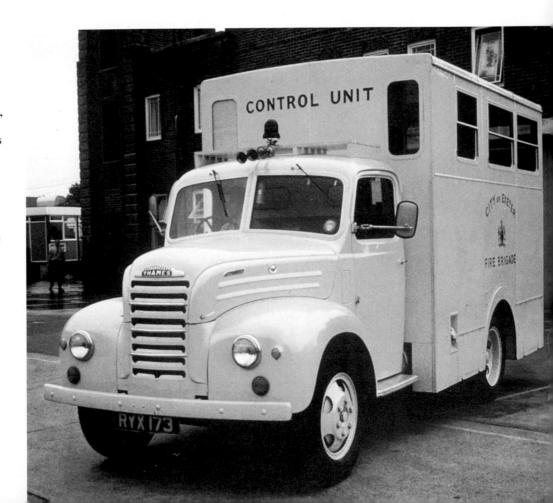

**RYX173, a Ford Thames, was used by the City of Exeter Fire Brigade at its Howell's Road station from 1956 as a Control Unit. It never passed to the Devon Fire Brigade as it was sold out of service in 1974. Many of these machines that were ordered by the Home Office were used as Control Units by other services around the country.**
*The Late John Hughes*

**Originally delivered to Hanley district of Stoke-on-Trent in 1976, this Ford D1617 chassied hydraulic platform was photographed when serving at Lammascote Road, Stafford. LVT462P was fitted with Simon SS263 booms. When Staffordshire Fire Brigade purchased a Scania-chassied Aerial Platform/Ladder supplied by Angloco the machine passed to Angloco as part of the deal.** *Clive Shearman*

| | | | | | Ford Chassied Specialist Appliances | |
|---|---|---|---|---|---|---|
| | | | | | | RYX-SXF series appliances are all ex Home Office stores. |
| NLB100 | | Salv/T | 52 | 64 | London Salvage Corps | Aldersgate London<br>Fordson 4D Thames-Wood & Lambert |
| NLB101 | | Salv/T | 53 | 69 | London Salvage Corps | Aldersgate London<br>Fordson 4D Thames-Wood & Lambert |
| NLB102 | | Salv/T | 54 | 67 | London Salvage Corps | Aldersgate London<br>Fordson 4D Thames-Wood & Lambert |
| NLB103 | | Salv/T | 55 | 68 | London Salvage Corps | Aldersgate-London<br>Fordson 4D Thames-Wood & Lambert |
| RYX112 | | C/Unit | 56 | 78 | Caernarvonshire Fire Brigade (Wales) | Llanberis Rd-Caernarfon<br>Thames-Home Office |
| RYX173 | | C/Unit | 56 | 74 | City of Exeter Fire Brigade | E32 Howell Rd-Exeter-**Yellow Livery**<br>Thames-Home Office |
| RYX278 | | Emerg/S C/Unit | 56 | 79 | Northumberland County Fire Brigade | A1 Loansdean-Morpeth-1979-**Emergency Services**<br>Thames-Home Office |
| SXF217 | | C/Unit | 56 | 79 | Teeside Fire Brigade | #1 Park Road South-Middlesbrough 1968<br>1 Park Road South-Middlesbrough 1979-Cleveland CFB<br>Thames-Home Office |
| SXF345 | | C/Unit | 56 | 79 | Shropshire Fire Service | St Michael's St-Shrewsbury-1979 -**Green livery**<br>Thames-Home Office |
| SXF348 | | C/Unit | 56 | 74 | Berkshire & Reading Fire Brigade | B1 Caversham Rd-Reading<br>Thames-Home Office |
| 683DXL | | WRC FOC | 56 | ? | Pembrokshire Fire Brigade (Wales) | ex Petrol Tanker-1968 /                    ?<br>Thames Trader-PFB |
| 684DXL | | WRC FOC | 56 | ? | Pembrokshire Fire Brigade (Wales) | ex Thames Trader-1968 /                    ?<br>Thames Trader-PFB |
| TTG461 | | FOT | 56 | 72 | Glamorgan County Fire Brigade (Wales) | C6 Heol y Nant-Whitchurch- ? / A2 Severn Sisters- ?<br>F4 Thames |
| TTG462 | | FOT | 56 | 71 | Glamorgan County Fire Brigade (Wales) | B4 Hazel Rd-Penarth - ? / C6 Whitchurch- ?<br>F4 Thames |
| TTG824 | | FOT | 56 | 72 | Glamorgan County Fire Brigade (Wales) | Bridgend Fire Station-1964/B1 Sunnyside-Bridgend-1972<br>F4 Thames |
| TTG825 | | FOT | 56 | 71 | Glamorgan County Fire Brigade (Wales) | A5 Station Rd-Port Talbot-1966 / A5 Commercial Rd-1972<br>F4 Thames |
| VTX800 | | FOC | 58 | 71 | Glamorgan County Fire Brigade (Wales) | B1 Bridgend-1964/B1 Sunnyside-Bridgend-? / C15 Abercynon<br>Thames Trader |
| YTX501 | | FOC | 58 | 72 | Glamorgan County Fire Brigade (Wales) | B6 Barry Fire Station<br>Thames Trader |
| YTX502 | | FOC | 58 | 72 | Glamorgan County Fire Brigade (Wales) | C1 Oxford St-Pontypridd<br>Thames Trader |
| 550BTX | | FOC | 59 | 72 | Glamorgan County Fire Brigade (Wales) | A5 Station Rd-Port Talbot-1966<br>A5 Commercial Rd-Port Talbot-1972<br>Thames Trader |
| UXM698 | | C/Unit | 62 | 78 | East Sussex Fire Brigade | South Rd-Haywards Heath-1971/A1 North St-Lewes-1978<br>Fordson 4D Thames-Home Office |
| YXC728 | | FOT | 60 | 75 | Pembrokeshire Fire Brigade (Wales) | **ex Petrol Tanker-1968** / Merlin's Wall-Haverfordwest-1974<br>B1 Haverfordwest-1975/Dyfed Fire Brigade<br>Thames Trader- |
| 611GUC | | Salv/T | 63 | 75 | London Salvage Corps | Aldersgate-London<br>Thames Trader-Wood & Lambert |
| CJJ612B | | Salv/T | 64 | 75 | London Salvage Corps | Aldersgate London<br>Thames Trader-Wood & Lambert |

288RFC is the only example of the Ford Thames Trader used as an emergency tender. Delivered in 1963 to Rewley Rd in the City of Oxford 288RFC served till being replaced by a pod system in 1978, though by then the brigade had become part of Oxfordshire Fire Service.
*Keith Wardell collection*

Considering how popular the Ford D Series was as a pump chassis, it is surprising that there were only six bodied as emergency tenders. Staffordshire also operated a near identical machine as a Foam/ Salvage Tender at Cannock.
*Michael Lawmon*

| | | | | | | |
|---|---|---|---|---|---|---|
| CDL306B | | WRC | 64 | 71 | Isle of Wight Fire Brigade | 1 South St-Newport<br>Thames Trader-IoWFB |
| HJF771D | | F/SalvT | 66 | 83 | City of Leicester | Lancaster Rd-Leicester<br>D500-Reeves Burgess |
| HKA799D | | Salv/T | 66 | ? | Liverpool Salvage Corps | Derby Road-Liverpool<br>D600-Davidson |
| LKB922E | | Salv/T | 67 | ? | Liverpool Salvage Corps | Derby Rd-Liverpool<br>D600-Davidson |
| NUU13E | | Salv/T | 67 | 77 | London Salvage Corps | Aldersgate London<br>Thames Trader-Wood & Lambert |
| KDF832E | | FOT | 67 | 78 | Gloucestershire Fire Service | 20 Severnside (Pilning)-1974/A4 Severnside (Pilning)-1978<br>A3 St Andrews Rd-Avonmouth-1981<br>B7 Tennis Court Rd-Kingswood-1983-County of Avon<br>**Foam equipment off Commer /Dennis M-DAD257C**<br>D600-HCB Angus/**Pyrene (Foam equipment)** |
| SYK714F | No-1 | Salv/T | 67 | 74 | London Salvage Corps | Aldersgate London-**Written off in RTA**<br>Thames Trader-Wood & Lambert |
| MHU303F | | Bulk Foam/C | 67 | 93 | Kent Fire Brigade | B43 Watling St-Rochester-Medway<br>D600-KFB |
| LDL543F | | WRC | 67 | 84 | Isle of White Fire Brigade | 9 Tennyson Rd-Freshwater /**Converted Tanker**<br>D600-IoWFB |
| SVK196G | | FOT | 69 | 85 | Newcastle & Gateshead Joint Fire Brigade | A3 West Rd-Newcastle-1974 /A High St-Newburn-1981<br>H York Rd-Whitley Bay-1985 /Tyne & Wear MFB<br>D300-Killingworth Koachworks |
| MKW544G | | C/Unit | 69 | 83 | Derbyshire Fire Service | A03 Derby Rd-Ripley<br>D300-Wilkes Mead |
| PDL29H | | WRC | 70 | | Isle of Wight Fire Brigade | **ex Gulley Emptier/**1 South St-Newport<br>D Series |
| DLK8J | FT.8 | FOT | 71 | 88 | London Fire Brigade | D27 London Rd-Heston-1980<br>D28 Faggs Rd-Feltham(Reserve)<br>D1000-Pyrene |
| DLK10J | HL .10 | HLL | 71 | 81 | London Fire Brigade | D30 Shepiston-Lane-Hayes<br>D800-Locomotors |
| AGG733J | | HLL | 71 | ? | Glasgow Fire Service (Scotland) | A1 Ingram St-Central-1975<br>D1010-JC Bennett |
| EOY907J | 1166 | Foam Tanker | 71 | 84 | Merseyside Fire Brigade | **ex Tanker-1978** / E1 Parr Stocks Rd-St Helens-1984<br>Merseyside Fire Brigade<br>D600- |
| NEX99J | | F/SalvT | 71 | 92 | Norfolk Fire Brigade | **ex WRL** /Kilhams Way-Kings Lynn<br>D1014-HCB Angus/NFB |
| ALV888K | | Salv/T | 71 | ? | Liverpool Salvage Corps | Derby Road-Liverpool<br>D600-Davidson |
| LTC730K | 116 | HLL | 71 | 85 | Lancashire County Fire Brigade | 9.1 Albert Rd-Farnworth-1974<br>B23 Albert Rd-Farnworth-1985/Greater Manchester CFS<br>D1314-Smith |
| LTC740K | 117 | FOT | 71 | 80 | Lancashire County  Fire Brigade | 11.2 Liverpool Rd-Eccles-1974<br>A13 Liverpool Rd-Eccles-1975<br>D46 Brownley Rd-Wythenshawe-1980<br>Greater Manchester CFS<br>D1314-Smith |
| KWY734K | | C/Unit | 71 | ? | West Riding of Yorkshire Fire Brigade | Headquarters<br>D1010-Anglo |
| KWY735K | | C/Unit | 71 | ? | West Riding of Yorkshire Fire Brigade | Bradford Rd-Keighley-1974<br>A17 Bradford Rd-Keighley/West Yorkshire Fire Service<br>D1010/Anglo |
| CPO635L | | BAT C/Unit | 72 | 96 | West Sussex Fire Brigade | A01 Ardsheal Rd-Worthing<br>D2817-Contact |

DLK10J was a unique 4x4 wheel drive appliance built on a Ford D800 Series chassis. It was a 1971 Locomotors-bodied Hose Layer that served the London Fire Brigade at Hayes fire station. Heathrow Airport is one of the station's risks.
*The late Alan Batchelor*

| CPO636L | | BAT C/Unit | 72 | 96 | West Sussex Fire Brigade | B12 Hurst Rd-Horsham D2817-Contact |
|---|---|---|---|---|---|---|
| CPO637L | | BAT C/Unit | 72 | 96 | West Sussex Fire Brigade | A17 Northgate-Chichester D2817-Contact |
| DDD700L | | Rec/V | 72 | | Gloucestershire Fire Service | ex Pump/E 12 Cheltenham /Brigade Workshops D1013-HCB Angus/GFS |
| LHS348L | | H/Fot | 72 | ? | Western Area Fire Brigade (Scotland) | Kings Rd-Johnstone-1975 C1 Kings Rd-Johnstone- Strathclyde Fire Brigade D400-Fulton & Wylie |
| HPW412L | | F/Salv | 72 | 92 | Norfolk Fire Brigade | ex WRL/High Rd-Gorleston D1014-ERF/NFB |
| UTC819M | 225 | HLL | 73 | 83 | Lancashire County Fire Brigade | B34/C54 Weldbank Rd-Chorley D1314-Smith |
| RAO1M | | FOT | 73 | 88 | Cumberland County Fire Brigade | ex WRT/Hensingham-Whitehaven-1984-1988 Cumbria Fire Service D1011-Gloster Saro |
| NRM666M | | FOT | 73 | 88 | Cumberland County Fire Brigade | ex WRL/Warwick St-Carlisle-1984-1988 Cumbria Fire Service D1013-Gloster Saro |
| RRA914M | | CAV | 73 | 90 | Derbyshire Fire Service | A02 Tamworth Rd-Long Eaton D0607-DFS |
| SHS721M | | H/FoT | 74 | ? | Western Area Fire Brigade (Scotland) | Canal St-Paisley-1975 C4 Canal St-Paisley-Strathclyde Fire Brigade D600-Fulton & Wylie |
| SHS722M | | H/Fot | 74 | ? | Western Area Fire Brigade (Scotland) | Rue End St-Greenock-1975 C7 Rue End St-Greenock-Strathclyde Fire Brigade D600-Fulton & Wylie |
| GFR218N | | PMover Artic/U | 74 | 83 | Greater Manchester County Fire Service | A12 Bolton Road-Agecroft-**Articulated Control Unit-** D1911-Entwhistles |
| GYM294N | BAT.1 | BAT | 74 | ? | London Fire Brigade | Brigade Headquarters-Lambeth R1014-Willowbrook |

| | | | | | | |
|---|---|---|---|---|---|---|
| GYM295N | BAT.2 | BAT | 74 | ? | London Fire Brigade | Brigade Headquarters-Lambeth<br>R1014-Willowbrook |
| HRA965N | | CIU | 75 | 88 | Derbyshire Fire Service | D1 Ascot Drive-Derby<br>D0710-Derby Commercials |
| XTC437N | 306 | FOT | 75 | 85 | Lancashire County Fire Brigade | D71 Byrom Rd-Blackburn<br>D1314-Carmichael |
| LUM999P | | HLL | 75 | ? | West Yorkshire Fire Service | E17 Green Lane Rawdon-Leeds<br>D Series |
| OYT517R | CU.7 | C/Unit | 77 | 85 | London Fire Brigade | Brigade Headquarters-Lambeth<br>R1014-Willowbrook-Anglo |
| TUA330R | | FOT | 77 | 91 | West Yorkshire Fire Service | C11 Outcote Bank-Huddersfield<br>D1314-Anglo |
| TBA260R | | Salv/T | 77 | | Greater Manchester County Fire Service | E53 Birch St-West Gorton-1981<br>E57 Railway St-Hyde-1987<br>**Conv Breathing Apparatus**-E57 Hyde-1993/ E56 Mossley-<br>D1114-Angloco |
| RCF243R | S5 | PM/P | 77 | 86 | Royal Berkshire Fire & Rescue Service | 03 Dee Rd-Reading<br>D1617- |
| UAX213S | | PM/P | 77 | 88 | Mid Glamorgan County Fire Brigade (Wales) | 01 Sunnyside-Bridgend<br>D1010- |
| VKG347S | | PMover | 77 | 88 | Mid Glamorgan County Fire Brigade (Wales) | 10 Llwnypria Rd-Tonypandy<br>D1010- |
| VKG348S | | PMover | 77 | 88 | Mid Glamorgan County Fire Brigade (Wales) | 01 Sunnyside-Bridgend-<br>D1010- |
| WBA544S | | FOT | 77 | 84 | Greater Manchester County Fire Service | A16 Cranleigh-Sale<br>D1617-Eagle |
| TYO470S | | Salv/T | 77 | 80 | London Salvage Corps | Aldersgate London<br>D1114-Cheshire FE |
| OKA70S | | Salv/T | 78 | 85 | Liverpool Salvage Corps | Derby Road-Liverpool<br>D0710-Harwin |
| RKC940T | | Salv/T | 78 | 85 | Liverpool Salvage Corps | Derby Road-Liverpool<br>D0710-Harwin |
| DLA345T | | Salv/T | 78 | 80 | London Salvage Corps | Aldersgate London<br>D1114- |
| FUR723T | | Foam/C | 78 | 93 | Hertfordshire County Council Fire Brigade | B11 Harpenden Rd-St Albans<br>D0907-HCCFB |
| ANC777T | | Salv/T | 78 | 93 | Greater Manchester County Fire Service | B20 Moor Lane-Bolton-1984<br>**Converted Breathing Apparatus/**B20 Bolton-1993<br>D1114-Angloco |
| DUB800T | | HLL | 78 | 90 | West Yorkshire Fire Service | B12 Lister St-Brighouse<br>D0907-Angloco |
| BND310T | | Hi ex FoT | 79 | 86 | Greater Manchester County Fire Service | B23 Albert Rd-Farnworth<br>D0710-Cocker |
| YHV182T | CIU.2 | CIU | 79 | 86 | London Fire Brigade | Brigade Headquarters-Lambeth<br>D0810-Hawson |
| TEM476V | | Salv/T | 79 | 85 | Liverpool Salvage Corps | Derby Road-Liverpool<br>D0710-Harwin |
| WHG207V | | PM FOC | 80 | 94 | Lancashire County Fire Brigade | C50 Blackpool Rd-Preston<br>D1314- |
| XCK590V | | PM CIU | 80 | 94 | Lancashire County Fire Brigade | C50 Blackpool Rd-Preston<br>D1010- |
| JVT471V | 505 | F/SalvT | 80 | | Staffordshire Fire Brigade | **ex Old Hednesford Rd-Cannock-1994**<br>**Conv to Damage Limitation Unit/**High St-Burton upon<br>Trent          D1114-Benson-SF&RS |
| CFT501V | T15 | DCU | 80 | 90 | Northumberland Fire Brigade | A1 Loansdean-Morpeth    D200-North Eastern CB |
| LNE536V | | FOT | 80 | 97 | Greater Manchester County Fire Service | D46 Brownley Rd-Wythenshawe-1992<br>D47 Turves Rd-Cheadle Hulme-<br>D1314-Cheshire FE |

| Reg | Fleet | Type | Year | Out | Fire Service | Details |
|---|---|---|---|---|---|---|
| GRJ298V | | FOT | 80 | 96 | Greater Manchester County Fire Service | E52 Briscoe Lane-Phillips Park-1996 D1314-Cheshire FE |
| XRV994V | S1 | PM /FOT C/Unit | 80 | 95? | Royal Berkshire Fire & Rescue Service | 18 London Rd-Langley D1617- |
| XOW193V | S4 | PM /BAT WRC | 80 | 95? | Royal Berkshire Fire & Rescue Service | 03 Dee Rd-Reading D1617-Novolift |
| XKB926W | 1197 | HLL Water/U | 80 | 94 | Merseyside Fire Brigade | C1 Studholme St-Bankhall D0907-Merseyside FB |
| XKB927W | 1198 | MPU | 80 | 94 | Merseyside Fire Brigade | **ex C1 Studholme St-Bankhall -1995**/ Reserve- D907-Merseyside FB-**Hiab 071** |
| DBP290W | S11 | PM CIU | 81 | 95? | Royal Berkshire Fire & Rescue Service | 02 Wokingham Rd-Reading D1617-Novolift |
| DMB721X | 1200 | HLL Water/U | 81 | 94 | Merseyside Fire Brigade | E1 Parr Stocks Rd-St Helens D0907-Merseyside FB |
| YFV360Y | | PM BAT | 82 | 95? | Lancashire County Fire Brigade | B71 Byrom Rd-Burnley Cargo 1721-Powell Duffryn |
| LAS160Y | | C/Unit | 83 | | Highlands & Islands Fire Brigade (Scotland) | A1 Harbour Rd-Inverness Cargo 1721-Wilcock-Seadyke |
| DWM607Y | 1211 | FOT | 83 | | Merseyside Fire Brigade | W1 Exmouth St-Birkenhead Cargo 1721-Malmo-MFB |
| A50HKC | 1219 | FOT | 84 | | Merseyside Fire Brigade | **ex E3 Huyton Lane-Huyton-1995**/ Training Centre- **Tank Re-chassied off Leyland Laird-EYE914J** Cargo 1721-Malmo-MFB |
| A518RRH | | C/Unit CAV | 84 | | Humberside Fire Brigade | **ex C7 Hose Layer-1990** A1 Worship St-Hull Central Cargo 1721-Derwent-HFB |
| A645CJR | 365 | PMover | 84 | | Tyne & Wear Metropolitan Fire Brigade | **Tynemouth or Sunderland ?** Cargo 1721-David Earl |
| A328SAT | | HLL | 84 | | Humberside Fire Brigade | **ex GPL & HGV** / C7 Holydyke Rd-Barton on Humber Cargo 1721-Hartford-HFB |
| B924KWM | 1230 | FOT | 85 | | Merseyside Fire Brigade | **ex C1 Bankhall-1991**/S5 Banks Rd-Liverpool Cargo 1721-Malmo-MFB |
| D182KKO | 820 | PMover BAU | 86 | | Kent Fire Brigade | **ex E16 Ladywell-Dover /ex E19 Park Farm Rd-Folkestone** Reserve- D1620-Multilift-Keyway |
| D183KKO | 821 | PMover ISU | 86 | | Kent Fire Brigade | **ex N43 Watling St-Rochester-Medway** N39 Gravesend Rd-Strood D1620-Multilift-Keyway |
| D184KKO | 822 | PMover ISU | 86 | | Kent Fire Brigade | **ex S60 Loose Rd-Maidstone-1996**/ Reserve- D1620-Multilift-Keyway |
| E581UKP | 823 | PM ISU | 87 | | Kent Fire Brigade | **ex E80 Upper Bridge St-Canterbury** / Reserve- D1620-Multilift-Keyway |
| E353VKM | 824 | PM/ ISU HLL | 87 | | Kent Fire Brigade | **ex N35 Coldharbour Rd-Northfleet-Thameside-1996** N84 Crescent Rd-Faversham- D1620-Multilift-Keyway |
| E352VKM | 825 | PMover HLL | 87 | | Kent Fire Brigade | **ex S60 Loose Rd-Maidstone-1996**/ Reserve D1620-Multi Lift-Keyway |
| E831XKE | 826 | PM /BAU ISU | 88 | | Kent Fire Brigade | E16 Ladywell-Dover D1620-Multi Lift-Keyway |
| E832XKE | 827 | PMover ICCU | 88 | | Kent Fire Brigade | **ex N43 Watling St-Rochester-Medway-1996** N45 St Michael's Rd-Sittingbourne - D1620-Multi Lift-Keyway |
| E833XKE | 828 | PMover ICCU | 88 | | Kent Fire Brigade | **ex N39 Gravesend Rd-Strood-1996** S72 Vale Rd-Tonbridge- D1620-Multi Lft-Keyway |
| E875ANO | | BAT | 88 | | Essex County Fire & Rescue Service | B34 Rainsford Lane-Chelmsford Iveco 60-10-EF&RS |
| F984XTG | | PMover | 88 | | Mid Glamorgan Fire Service-**1996** South Wales Fire Service (Wales) | Training Centre Iveco Cargo 1415-Powell Duffryn |

| Reg | Fleet No | Type | Year | Fire Service | Details |
|---|---|---|---|---|---|
| F985XTG | | PMover Salv/T WRC | 88 | Mid Glamorgan Fire Service-**1996** South Wales Fire Service (Wales) | 01 Angel St-Sunnyside-Bridgend Iveco Cargo 1415-Powell Duffryn |
| F183OKE | 829 | PMover | 89 | Kent Fire Brigade | **ex E80 Upper Bridge St-Canterbury-1996/** Reserve D1620-Multilift-Keyway |
| G87SNL | | ISU | 90 | Northumberland Fire & Rescue Service | CD Cowpen Rd-Blyth Iveco 65-12-Zeta |
| G888TKN | 851 | Bulk/Wrc | 90 | Kent Fire Brigade | S11 Canterbury Rd-Ashford Iveco Cargo 1721-Boughton |
| G826TKP | 852 | Bulk/Wrc | 90 | Kent Fire Brigade | S56 New Hythe Rd-Larkfield Iveco Cargo 1721-Boughton |
| H197GKM | A00056 | WRC | 91 | West Sussex Fire Brigade | 07 Maltravers Rd-Littlehampton **Tank off Bedford TK-AMY708H** Iveco Cargo 1721-Boughton |
| H286UGP | | HLL | 91 | Buckinghamshire Fire & Rescue Service | **ex Newport Pagnell-1992/**Cambridge St-Aylesbury Iveco 4x4-Chambers Engineering |
| H788GAR | | HLL | 91 | Essex Fire & Rescue Service | **ex C52 Broadmayne-Basildon-1995** W68 Laindon Rd-Billericay- Iveco Cargo 1721-John Dennis CB |
| J782PKX | W090 | Support Unit | 92 | Hertfordshire County Council Fire Brigade | B11 Harpenden Rd-St Albans Iveco Cargo 0915-Leicester Carriage Builders |
| J783PKX | W087 | GPV | 92 | Hertfordshire County Council Fire Brigade | C23 Stevenage Iveco Cargo 0915-Leicester Carriage Builders |
| J350CNU | | BAT | 91 | Nottinghamshire Fire & Rescue Service | 22 Station Rd-Beeston Iveco Ford 79-14-Mellor-NF&RS |
| K578YAX | | PMover | 92 | Mid Glamorgan Fire Service-**1996** South Wales Fire Service (Wales) | Fire Prevention Department Iveco 49-12-Keillor Trailer |
| K355MPO | | PMover | 93 | Hampshire Fire & Rescue Service | Driving School Iveco Cargo 110E15-Ray Smith |
| K873BBH | W093 | Haz Mat | 93 | Hertfordshire Fire & Rescue Service | A01 Queensway-Hemel Hempstead Iveco Cargo 100E18-Leicester Carriage Builders |
| L689GVS | 30 | C/Unit | 93 | Bedfordshire Fire & Rescue Service | 10 Dunstable Rd-Toddington Iveco Cargo 75-GC Smith |
| M268XOT | | PMover | 94 | Hampshire Fire & Rescue Service | Headquarters Iveco Cargo 120E15-Ray Smith |
| M477XCR | A00152 | BAT Support/U | 95 | West Sussex Fire Brigade | B12 Hurst Rd-Horsham Iveco Super Cargo 170E23-Leicester Carriage Builders |
| M478XCR | A00153 | BAT Support/U | 95 | West Sussex Fire Brigade | A17 Northgate-Chichester Iveco Super Cargo 170E23-Leicester Carriage Builders |
| N335PNH | W097 | DC/Unit | 95 | Hertfordshire Fire & Rescue Service | C32 Newton Way-Hitchin Iveco Cargo 100E18-Leicester Carriage Builders |
| N109EBP | | MRV | 95 | Hampshire Fire & Rescue Service | D48 Southampton Rd-Lyndhurst Iveco Cargo 135E18-Angloco-**HIAB 071** |
| N502VNH | W098 | DC/Unit | 96 | Hertfordshire Fire & Rescue Service | A07 Rectory Rd-Rickmansworth Iveco Cargo 100E18-Leicester Carriage Builders |
| N142DPX | A00154 | BAT Support/U | 96 | West Sussex Fire Brigade | 05 Stoney Lane-Shoreham on Sea Iveco Super Cargo 170E23-Leicester Carriage Builders |
| N189YJM | | CI/Unit | 96 | Mid & West Wales Fire Brigade (Wales) | Llandiloes Rd-Newtown Iveco Turbo Daily-M&WWFB |
| P114PAG | | C/Unit | 96 | Humberside Fire Brigade | Iveco Cargo 100E18-G. C. Smith |
| P912KPX | | Multi/RU | 96 | Hampshire Fire & Rescue Service | A02 Lynchford Rd-Farnborough-Rushmoor -Multi Role Unit Iveco Cargo 135E18-Angloco-**HIAB 071** |
| P913KPX | | Multi/RU | 97 | Hampshire Fire & Rescue Service | C29 Steel Close-Eastleigh-Multi Role Unit Iveco Cargo 135E18-Angloco-**HIAB 071** |

| Types A0610 A0609 A040 | | | | | Ford A Series Specialist Appliances | The A Series was in the light to middle range of van/lorry chassis. It was 3.5 to 5.5 tons. and was powered by a 2.4 litre diesel engine. |
|---|---|---|---|---|---|---|
| HFH617N | | C/Unit | 74 | 90 | Gloucestershire Fire Service | 05 Eastern Ave-Gloucester A0610-Hicks |
| LRF932P | | C/Unit | 76 | 88 | Staffordshire Fire Brigade | Uttoxeter Rd-Longton A040-Reeves Burgess |
| SMB670R | | CIU | 76 | 92 | Cheshire Fire Brigade | B4 Heath Rd-Runcorn-1992 A0609-ERF |
| VRN151R | 367 | Res/T | 77 | 84 | Lancashire County Fire Brigade | 6.1/E94 Bradley Rd-Nelson A0609-Cheshire FE |
| VRN152R | 368 | Res/T | 77 | 84 | Lancashire County Fire Brigade | 5.1/D70 Manchester Rd-Accrington A0609-Cheshire FE |
| VRN153R | 369 | Res/T | 77 | 84 | Lancashire County Fire Brigade | 2.2/A11 Cable St-Lancaster A0609-Cheshire FE |
| UUJ724S | | Res/T | 77 | 89 | Shropshire Fire Service | St Michael's St-Shrewsbury-1989 A0610-Cheshire FE |
| OTR215S | A00313 | C/Unit | 77 | 97? | West Sussex Fire Brigade | 20 West Meads Drive-Bognor Regis A0609-Hawson Garner-WSFB |
| WWR659S | | ET | 78 | 89 | West Yorkshire Fire Service | A15 Highfield Rd-Idle-Bradford A0610-Cheshire FE |
| WWR660S | | ET | 78 | 89 | West Yorkshire Fire Service | F11 Brunswick St-Wakefield A0610-Cheshire FE |
| DTU346S | | BAT | 78 | ? | Cheshire Fire Brigade | A1 St Annes St-Chester A0609-Garner |
| DTU347S | | Salv/T | 78 | 92 | Cheshire Fire Brigade | A5 Sadler-Rd-Winsford A0609-Garner |
| DTU349S | | CIU | 78 | 92 | Cheshire Fire Brigade | C9 West St-Congleton A0609-Garner |
| WUX348S | | Res/T | 78 | 89 | Shropshire Fire Service | Haybridge Rd-Wellington-1984 /Reserve-1989 A0610-Cheshire FE |
| TCJ557S | | Res/T | 78 | 96 | Powys Fire Service (Wales) | 10 Camden Rd-Brecon A0610-Cheshire FE |
| TCR341T | A00301 | CAV | 78 | 95 | West Sussex Fire Brigade | 20 West Meads Drive-Bognor Regis A0609-Garner |
| AAJ195T | 87 | ET | 78 | 87 | North Yorkshire Fire Brigade | C5 Crosby Rd-Northallerton-1981 A8 Broughton Rd-Skipton-1987 A0610-Angloco |
| AAJ196T | 88 | ET | 78 | 87 | North Yorkshire Fire Brigade | D1 Clifford St-York A0610-Angloco |
| BNG480T | | Res/T | 78 | 92 | Norfolk Fire Brigade | B47 Kilhams Way-Kings Lynn-1983 B54 Norwich Rd-Thetford-1992 A0610-Cheshire FE |
| BNG481T | | Res/T | 78 | 92 | Norfolk Fire Brigade | C69 Friars Lane-Great Yarmouth-1986 B44 Norwich Rd-Fakenham-1992 A0610-Cheshire FE |
| DUB801T | | ET | 78 | 90 | West Yorkshire Fire Service | B11 Skircoat Moor Rd-Halifax-1984 B13 South Lane-Elland-1987 A0610-Cheshire FE |
| DUB802T | | ET | 78 | 89 | West Yorkshire Fire Service | C11 Outcote Bank-Huddersfield A0610-Cheshire FE |
| HMN999 | | Res/T | 79 | | Isle of Man Fire Brigade | 1 Peel Rd-Douglas-1992/3 Station Rd-Ramsey A0610-Cheshire FE |
| ETL416T | | Res/T | 79 | 92 | Lincolnshire Fire Brigade | A1 South Park Ave-Lincoln-1983 B1 Churchill Ave-Skegness-1992 A0609-Angloco |

| | | | | | | |
|---|---|---|---|---|---|---|
| FFE504T | | Res/T | 79 | 91 | Lincolnshire Fire Brigade | C1 Robins Hood Walk-Boston<br>A0609/Angloco |
| FFE505T | | Res/T | 79 | 90 | Lincolnshire Fire Brigade | D1 Harloxton Road-Grantham<br>A0609-Angloco |
| CAD319T | | Foam/C | 79 | **95?** | Gloucestershire Fire Service | 07 Pagenhill Lane-Stroud<br>A0610-Dormobile |
| ENV151T | | Res/T | 79 | 90 | Northamptonshire Fire Brigade | B4 Staverton Rd-Daventry<br>A0610-Cheshire FE |
| EVN62V | **94** | ET | 79 | 89 | North Yorkshire Fire Service | A1 Skipton Rd-Harrogate<br>A0610-Angloco |
| GFH951V | | Salv/T | 80 | 94 | Gloucestershire Fire Service | 12 Keynsham Rd-Cheltenham<br>A0610-Hicks |
| KNK442V | **W054** | Dec/U | 80 | 93 | Hertfordshire County Council<br>Fire Brigade | A01 Queensway-Hemel Hempstead<br>A0610-Longwell Green |
| FAW13V | **43** | C/Unit | 80 | 96 | Shropshire Fire Service | St Michael's St-Shrewsbury<br>A0610-HCB Angus |
| FAW14V | | CIU | 80 | 93 | Shropshire Fire Service | St Michael's St-Shrewsbury-1982/Stafford Park-Telford-1993<br>A0610-Anglo |
| XOT151V | **A00337** | C/Unit | 80 | | West Sussex Fire Brigade | 24 Mill Green Rd-Haywards Heath<br>A0609-Hawson Garner-WSFB |
| HPH946V | | C/Unit | 80 | | Surrey Fire Brigade | **ED12 Spook Hill-Dorking -1993**/ 35 Walton on Thames-<br>A0609-Cocker |
| WSM815V | | ET | 80 | **95?** | Dumfries & Galloway Fire Brigade<br>(Scotland) | D1 Brooms Rd-Dumfries<br>**Converted to Incident Support Unit**<br>A0610-Angloco |
| WSM536V | | ET | 80 | **95?** | Dumfries & Galloway Fire Brigade<br>(Scotland) | B6 Arthur St-Newton Stewart<br>**Converted to Incident Support Unit**<br>A0610-Angloco |
| BFO308V | | Res/T | 80 | 96 | Powys Fire Service<br>(Wales) | 01 Llanidloes Rd-Newtown<br>A0610-Angloco |

**Northamptonshire operated four Rescue Tenders based on the Ford A Series. When photographed, this 1981 example was operating as a Chemical Incident unit allocated to Rushden near the M1 motorway. It had previously served as a Rescue Tender at Wellingborough. Others of the type were allocated to Daventry, Northampton and Kettering.**
*Clive Shearman*

| | | | | | | |
|---|---|---|---|---|---|---|
| BDE800V | | ET | 80 | 90 | Dyfed Fire Brigade (Wales) | A1 Corporation Ave-Llanelli<br>A0610-Carmichael |
| NGD16V | | ESU | 80 | 88 | Strathclyde Fire Brigade (Scotland) | E2 Dellburn St-Motherwell<br>A0610-F&Wylie |
| NGD17V | | ESU | 80 | 87 | Strathclyde Fire Brigade (Scotland) | A2 Grudie St-Easterhouse-Glasgow<br>A0610-F&Wylie |
| LNW880V | | BAT | 80 | ? | West Yorkshire Fire Service | Brigade Headquarters<br>A0610-Angloco |
| SGG689W | | ESU | 80 | 86 | Strathclyde Fire Brigade (Scotland) | B1 South Fire Station-Glasgow<br>A0610-F&Wylie |
| SGG690W | | ESU | 80 | 87 | Strathclyde Fire Brigade (Scotland) | F7 Castlegreen St-Dumbarton<br>A0610-F&Wylie |
| SGG691W | | ESU | 80 | 87 | Strathclyde Fire Brigade (Scotland) | C5 Paisley Rd-Renfrew<br>A0610-F&Wylie |
| SGG692W | | ESU | 80 | 87 | Strathclyde Fire Brigade (Scotland) | D1 Station Rd-Ayr<br>A061-F&Wylie |
| EBX800W | | ET | 80 | 90 | Dyfed Fire Brigade (Wales) | B1 Merlins Wall-Haverfordwest<br>A0610-Carmichael |
| EBX801W | | ET | 80 | 90 | Dyfed Fire Brigade (Wales) | C1 Trefechan-Aberystyth<br>A0610-Carmichael |
| JDC471W | 98 | ET | 80 | 89 | North Yorkshire Fire Brigade | B1 North Marine Rd-Scarborough<br>A0610-Angloco |
| MAJ106W | 100 | ET | 81 | 92 | North Yorkshire Fire Brigade | C5 Crosby Rd-Northallerton-1988 /Reserve-1991<br>A0610-Angloco |
| TRH281W | | C/Unit | 81 | 88 | Humberside Fire Brigade | A1 Worship St-Hull<br>A0610-Benson |
| VNV338W | | Res/T | 81 | 91 | Northamptonshire Fire Brigade | B1 The Mounts-Northampton<br>A0610-A.E.Smith |
| VNV339W | | Res/T | 81 | 90 | Northamptonshire Fire Brigade | A10 Irthlingborough Rd-Wellingborough<br>**Converted Chemical Incident Unit**<br>A12 Newton Rd-Rushden-1990<br>A0610-A.E.Smith |
| PFJ274W | 5304 | HLL | 81 | | Devon County Fire Brigade | 01 North Rd-Barnstaple-<br>A0609-G&T Attack- **4x4 conv by Newton Abbot Motors** |
| AVV917X | | Res/T | 81 | 90 | Northamptonshire Fire Brigade | A1 The Headlands-Kettering<br>A0610-Cheshire FE |
| OWJ826X | | Res/T | 81 | 95 | South Yorkshire County Fire Service | D2 Oaks Lane-Rotherham-1988/Training Centre-1995<br>A0610-Cheshire FE |
| VWR819X | | ET | 82 | ? | West Yorkshire Fire Service | D12 Girton Approach-Gipton<br>A0610-Cheshire FE |
| VWR820X | | Salv/T | 82 | ? | West Yorkshire Fire Service | E12 Stanningley Rd-Bramley<br>A0610-Angloco |
| VWR821X | | C/Unit | 82 | ? | West Yorkshire Fire Service | Brigade Headquarters<br>A0610-Angloco |
| CWY154Y | | ET | 82 | ? | West Yorkshire Fire Service | D16 Walton Rd-Wetherby-1984/F15 Hazel Rd-Knottingley-<br>A0610-Angloco |
| CWY155Y | | ET | 82 | 91 | West Yorkshire Fire Service | C13 Hightown Rd-Cleckheaton<br>A0610-Angloco |
| CWY156Y | | ET | 82 | ? | West Yorkshire Fire Service | A17 Bradford Rd-Keighley<br>A0610-Angloco |
| TUH893Y | | ET | 82 | 91 | Mid Glamorgan Fire Brigade (Wales) | 01 Sunnyside-Bridgend-1985/Reserve-1991<br>A0610-Merryweather |
| CDV77Y | | HLL | 83 | | Devon County Fire Brigade | 33 Church Rd-Exmouth<br>A0609-F&Wylie- **4x4 conversion -Newton Abbot Motors** |
| A595XWE | | Res/T | 83 | 93 | South Yorkshire County Fire Service | B3 Edlington Lane-Edlington<br>A0610-Saxon |
| A596XWE | | Res/T | 83 | 93 | South Yorkshire County Fire Service | B4 Union Rd-Thorne<br>A0610-Saxon |

| Transit types Custom 115/130/160 175/180/250 | | | | | Ford Transit Chassied Appliances | The Transit was the successor to the 15cwt Thames van. It had 6 different payload categories. The larger ones had twin rear wheels. They were powered by a range of petrol and diesel engines from 2.0 litre up to the modern 2.9 fuel injected versions. |
|---|---|---|---|---|---|---|
| WJH58E | | Res/T | 67 | 73 | Hertfordshire County Council Fire Brigade | B24 Victoria St-Hertford 180-HCFB |
| JHH942E | | E/Unit | 67 | 73 | Carlisle Fire Service | Warwick St-Carlisle 160-CFB |
| SLK36F | BACV-36 | BApC | 68 | 80 | GLC London Fire Brigade | Brigade Headquarters-Lambeth |
| SWD238G | | F/Salv | 69 | 83 | Warwick County Fire Brigade | 41 Warwick St-Leamington Spa-1977 /**Converted to ET** 51 Mason's Ave-Stratford on Avon-1983 **Converted to BApT** /29 Warwick St-Leamington Spa-1987 160-WCFB |
| XYB851H | | L2P | 70 | | Somerset Fire Brigade | 03 St Cuthberts Way-Dulverton 160-SFB |
| WAC509H | | ET | 70 | 83 | Warwick County Fire Brigade | 23 Park Rd-Coleshill 160-WCFB |
| | | | | | | **All London Fire Brigade small Transit Control Vehicles were built on the 130 chassis** |
| EGH37J | BACV-37 | BApC | 71 | 80 | GLC London Fire Brigade | D21 Uxbridge Rd-Ealing |
| EGH38J | BACV-38 | BApC | 71 | 80 | GLC London Fire Brigade | A21 Harrow Rd-Paddington |
| EGH39J | BACV-39 | BApC | 71 | 80 | GLC London Fire Brigade | E21 High St-Lewisham |
| ELN40J | BACV-40 | BApC | 71 | 80 | GLC London Fire Brigade | L21 High St-East Ham |
| AUT957K | | CAV | 71 | 86 | City of Leicester | C2 Aikman Ave-Leicester Western-1974 N24 Leicester Western-1984/Brigade Headquarters-1986 Leicestershire Fire Service 130-CLFB |
| HNY687K | | Salv/T | 71 | | Glamorgan County Fire Brigade (Wales) | B6 Barry Fire Station-1974 3 Heol-y-Nant-Whitchurch-1985  South Glamorgan F&RS 130-GCFB |
| BTY223K | | C/Unit | 71 | 82 | Northumberland County Fire Brigade | A1 Loansdean-Morpeth 130-NCFB |
| JLT41K | BACV-41 | BApC | 72 | 80 | GLC London Fire Brigade | F21 Romford Rd-Stratford |
| JLT42K | BACV-42 | BApC | 72 | 80 | GLC London Fire Brigade | G21 Pinner Rd-Harrow |
| JYH43K | BACV-43 | BApC | 72 | 85 | GLC London Fire Brigade | B21 Old Town-Clapham |
| JLT125K | HEF-1 | Hi Ex Foam/U | 72 | 84 | GLC London Fire Brigade | C21 Old St-Shoreditch-1983 B26 Old Kent Road-Old Kent Rd-1984 |
| JYD527K | | Accident Unit | 72 | 80 | Somerset Fire Brigade | Milton Ave-Weston Super Mare-1974 C1 Weston Super Mare-County of Avon-1980 130-SFB |
| PPA759L | | CAV | 72 | | Surrey County Fire Brigade | **Originally a Foam Salvage Tender** / Brigade Headquarters |
| PPH14L | | DCU | 72 | | Surrey County Fire Brigade | **ex Hose Layer** / E12 Spook Hill-Dorking N33 Addlestone-Chertsey / E10 Croyden Rd-Reigate 130-Hawson/SFB |
| HUR61L | | Salv/T | 72 | 81 | Hertfordshire County Council Fire Brigade | A01 Queensway-Hemel Hempstead-**Conv Chemical Incident**      180-HCFB |
| ONK74L | | BApC | 72 | | Hertfordshire County Council Fire Brigade | B24 Victoria St-Hertford 180-HCFB |
| CHH999L | | Res/T | 73 | 78 | Carlisle Fire Brigade | Warwick St-Carlisle-1974   **Converted  into Chemical Incident Unit** -1978-Cumbria FS      130-CFB |
| MLX44L | BACV-44 | BApC | 73 | 83 | GLC London Fire Brigade | C21 Old St-Shoreditch |
| MLX45L | BACV-45 | BApC | 73 | 83 | GLC London Fire Brigade | H31 Old Town-Croydon |
| MLX46L | BACV-46 | BApC | 73 | 83 | GLC London Fire Brigade | J21 Church St-Edmonton |
| MLX47L | BACV-47 | BApC | 73 | 83 | GLC London Fire Brigade | K21 Kingston Rd-Wimbledon |
| HPM965L | | Res/T | 73 | 84 | East Sussex Fire Brigade | B12 Keld Ave-Uckfield 250-HCB Angus |
| HPM966L | | Res/T | 73 | 84 | East Sussex Fire Brigade | B18 London Rd-Battle 250-HCB Angus |

| | | | | | | |
|---|---|---|---|---|---|---|
| ODN193M | No.7 | F/SalvT | 73 | 84 | City of York | #1 Clifford St-York-1974 /D4 Canal Rd-Selby-1984 175- |
| YTU184M | | CAV | 73 | 90 | Cheshire Fire Brigade | A4 Braddon Close-Northwich 130-ERF |
| RAX951M | | C/Unit | 73 | 82 | Monmouthshire Fire Brigade (Wales) | New Inn-Pontypool-1974 / B19-Pontypool-1982 Gwent FB 160-NCBFB |
| XYC605M | | Accident Unit | 74 | 84 | Somerset Fire Brigade | 01 Lisieux Way-Taunton 130-SFB |
| YBF221M | 115 | Res/T | 74 | 84 | Staffordshire Fire Brigade | Knutton Lane-Newcastle under Lyne-1976 Giggetty Lane-Wombourne-1984 115-SFB |
| KYA428N | | C/Unit | 74 | 91 | Somerset Fire Brigade | 02 Salmon Parade-Bridgwater 130-SFB |
| KYA429N | | C/Unit | 74 | 91 | Somerset Fire Brigade | 21 Reckleford-Yeovil 130-SFB |
| HWC423N | | BAT | 74 | 82 | Essex County Fire Brigade | C51 North Rd-Brentwood 160-ECFB |
| GVD269N | | CAV | 74 | | Hertfordshire County Council Fire Brigade | A01Queensway-Hemel Hempstead B19 Bridge Rd-Welwyn Garden City 180-HCFB |
| LAX119P | | Res/T | 76 | 85 | South Glamorgan County Fire Service (Wales) | 04 Heol-y-Nant-Whitchurch-1984 07 Druids Green-Cowbridge-1985 160-Hoskins |
| KAS48P | | RRU | 76 | 87 | Highlands & Islands Fire Brigade (Scotland) | A1 Harbour Rd-Inverness 160-HCB Angus |
| ORE561P | | Res/T | 76 | 90 | Staffordshire Fire Brigade | Knutton Lane-Newcastle under Lyne 130-Carmichael |
| MMO106P | | Res/T | 76 | 82 | Berkshire & Reading Fire Brigade | A16 Downshire Way-Bracknell |
| NKE181P | | Res/T | 76 | 80 | East Sussex Fire Brigade | 04 Preston Circus-Brighton/**Written off in RTA** 250-Branbridge |
| TRE350R | | Res/T | 77 | 85 | Staffordshire Fire Brigade | Birmingham Rd-Lichfield-1985 Giggetty Lane-Wombourne-1988/Reserve-1994 160-Anglo |

**Surrey Fire Brigade had a superb fleet of coach-built appliances. Based on Ford Transit chassis, PPH14L, was a 1972 example that formed a Hawson-bodied Damage Control Unit working out of Dorking. A sister machine ran as a Canteen Van though that unit started out as a Foam Salvage Tender.**
*Michael Lawmon*

| | | | | | | |
|---|---|---|---|---|---|---|
| YBF838S | 130 | Res/T | 78 | 85 | Staffordshire Fire Brigade | Springfield Rd-Leek-1988<br>Giggetty Lane-Wombourne-1991/Reserve-1994<br>160-Cheshire FE |
| YHV211T | DCU-1 | Divisional C/Unit | 79 | ? | GLC London Fire Brigade | B21 Old Town-Clapham-1984<br>Transfered Media Resources Group<br>160-LFB |
| YHV212T | DCU-2 | Divisional C/Unit | 79 | ? | GLC London Fire Brigade | D21 Uxbridge Rd-Ealing<br>160-LFB |
| YHV213T | DCU-3 | Divisional C/Unit | 79 | ? | GLC London Fire Brigade | A21 Harrow Rd-Paddington -1984<br>Transfered Media Resources Group<br>160-LFB |
| YHV214T | DCU-4 | Divisional C/Unit | 79 | ? | GLC London Fire Brigade | E21 High St-Lewisham<br>160-LFB |
| YHV215T | DCU-5 | Divisional C/Unit | 79 | ? | GLC London Fire Brigade | L21 High St-East Ham<br>160-LFB |
| YHV232T | FIU-2 | FIU | 79 | ? | GLC London Fire Brigade | Brigade Headquarters-Lambeth<br>160-LFB |
| CYV876V | DCU-6 | Divisional C/Unit | 80 | ? | GLC London Fire Brigade | F22 East India Docks Rd-Poplar-1984<br>Transfered Media Resource Group<br>160-LFB |
| CYV877V | DCU-7 | Divisional C/Unit | 80 | ? | GLC London Fire Brigade | G30 Harrow Rd-Wembley<br>160-LFB |
| CYV878V | DCU-8 | Divisional C/Unit | 80 | ? | GLC London Fire Brigade | C21 Old St-Shoreditch<br>160-LFB |
| KYA876V<br>KYC876V | | A/Unit | 80 | 89 | Somerset Fire Brigade | 21 Reckleford-Yeovil<br>160-SFB |
| MRA579W | | CIU | 81 | 88 | Derbyshire Fire Service | C1 Sheffield Rd-Chesterfield<br>180-DFB |
| MPD474W | | SRV | 81 | 92 | Surrey County Council Fire Brigade | E12 Spook Hill-Dorking<br>100-SFB |
| MUH545X | | C/Unit | 82 | | Gwent Fire Brigade-**1996**<br>South Wales Fire Service (Wales) | B19 New Rd-New Inn-Pontypool -1993<br>**Converted to Canteen Van-**B16 Hereford Rd-Abergavenny<br>180-Merryweather |
| PKU738X | | Res/T | 82 | | South Yorkshire County Fire Service | **ex E3Mansfield Rd-Sheffield-1984/Training-1993**/ Res-<br>160-Angloco |
| BPG771Y | | Res/T | 83 | 90 | Surrey County Council Fire Brigade | E19 Eastbourne Rd-Godstone<br>130-SCCFB |
| BPG772Y | | Res/T | 83 | 90 | Surrey County Council Fire Brigade | W29 Church St-Woking<br>130-SCCFB |
| BPG773Y | | Res/T | 83 | 94 | Surrey County Council Fire Brigade | N33 Addlestone-Chertsey<br>130-SCCFB |
| KST960Y | | FOT | 83 | | Highlands & Islands Fire Brigade (Scotland) | A1 Harbour Rd-Inverness<br>2.0-H&IFB |
| VKY559Y | | Res/T | 83 | 93 | South Yorkshire County Fire Service | B2 Quarry Lane-Adwick le Street<br>160 County-Angloco |
| A539WNP | | ISU | 84 | 94 | Hereford & Worcester Fire Brigade | 46 Owen St-Hereford<br>100-H&WFB |
| B47CKY | | Res/T | 84 | | South Yorkshire County Fire Service | **ex E3 Mansfield Rd-Sheffield-1993**<br>**ex B2 Quarry Lane-Adwick le Street-1995**/ Training-<br>160 County-Angloco |
| C643KCE | | CIU | 86 | 94 | Cambridgeshire Fire & Rescue Service | B13 Huntingdon St-St Neots<br>160 2.0-CF&RS |
| C158GSJ | | RRU | 86 | 94 | Strathclyde Fire Brigade (Scotland) | B05 Calder St-Polmadie-1992 /Reserve-1994<br>180-SFB |
| C159GSJ | | RRU | 86 | 94 | Strathclyde Fire Brigade (Scotland) | A02 Grudie St-Easterhouse-1990<br>A05 Anniesland-Knightswood-1992          180-SFB |
| C411CKR | | ET | 86 | **89?** | Kent Fire Brigade | C60 Loose Rd-Maidstone<br>160 County 4x4-Keyway |

The Ford Transit proved immensely popular as a specialist appliance chassis. Based on the 160 series, TRE350R was fitted with Angloco bodywork and served out of Lichfield fire station in Staffordshire. It was replaced by a Rescue Tender based on the Jeep J20, a type that found favour with Staffordshire. TRE350R was one of four rescue tenders to serve the county, the others were allocated to Newcastle under Lyne, Leek and Wombourne. *Michael Lawmon*

| C412CKR | | ET | 86 | **89?** | Kent Fire Brigade | D80 Upper Bridge St-Canterbury<br>160 County 4x4-Keyway |
|---|---|---|---|---|---|---|
| C413CKR | | ET | 86 | **89?** | Kent Fire Brigade | E35 Cold Harbour Rd-Northfleet Thameside<br>160 County 4x4-Keyway |
| D377RGG | | RRU | 87 | 94 | Strathclyde Fire Brigade<br>(Scotland | C05 Paisley Rd-Renfrew<br>2.8i-SFB |
| E757EPM | | BAT | 87 | | Surrey Fire & Rescue Service | Brigade Headquarters<br>2.0-SF&RS |
| E263LBX | | PMover<br>C/Unit | 87 | | Dyfed County Fire Brigade-**1996**<br>Mid & West Wales FB (Wales) | B6/W16 High St-Pembroke Dock /**Articulated Unit**<br>120-Lyntoa |
| E460SSD | | RRU | 88 | | Strathclyde Fire Brigade<br>(Scotland) | E02 Delburn St-Motherwell<br>2.8i-SFB |
| E461SSD | | RRU | 88 | 96 | Strathclyde Fire Brigade<br>(Scotland) | F07 Castlegreen St-Dumbarton<br>2.8i-SFB |
| F459UEF | | Res/T | 88 | | Cleveland County Fire Brigade-**1996**<br>Cleveland Fire Brigade | Reserve-<br>2.8i-CCFB |
| F282OLE | | L2P<br>Res/T | 89 | | Buckinghamshire Fire & Rescue<br>Service | High St-Whitchurch-1993 /Reserve<br>2.8i-LWB-Mountain Range |
| F268WCS | | RRU | 89 | | Strathclyde Fire Brigade<br>(Scotland) | E14 Carlisle Rd-Lesmahagow<br>2.8i-SFB |
| G139CBY | | Res/T | 89 | | Cleveland County Fire Brigade-**1996**<br>Cleveland Fire Brigade | Reserve-<br>2.8i-CCFB |
| G282APF | | SR/Unit | 89 | | Surrey Fire & Rescue Service | 11 Croydon Rd-Reigate<br>2.8I-SF&RS |
| G917OTO | | BAT | 90 | | Isle of Wight Fire Brigade | 04 Station St-Ryde<br>2.8i-IoWF&RS |
| G839DCS | | RRU | 90 | | Strathclyde Fire Brigade<br>(Scotland) | F22 Oban Rd-Inveraray<br>2.8i-SFB |
| N665WVR | | Canteen/<br>V | 95 | | Greater Manchester<br>County Fire Service | B20 Crompton Way-Bolton<br>VE6-Ford-Bedwas |
| N951NUF | | CS/Unit | 96 | | East Sussex County Fire Brigade | 11 Whitley Rd-Eastbourne<br>VE6-Ford-ESCFB |

**SVK196G, a very rare Ford D300 Series Foam Tender, served the Newcastle & Gateshead Joint Fire Service from 1969, when it was delivered to one of the Newcastle stations. The appliance served at a number of stations within that brigade, but ended its time at Whitley Bay in 1985 with the Tyne & Wear Metropolitan Fire Brigade.** *Ian Moore*

| Chassis 2 Ton Wheelbase 9 ft 10 ins | | | | | Fordson Thames 7V Chassis Engine 30hp V8 cylinder petrol Pump Sulzer 800 gpm | The War Department ordered vast numbers of the Fordson 2 ton normal control chassis for use as pumpers and other vehicles for use in the newly formed NFS (National Fire Service. Large numbers passed to the local authority brigades at the end of hostilities. Fire Station name only noted as details are sketchy as these appliances moved around. |
|---|---|---|---|---|---|---|
| GTC10 | | ET | 37 | 54 | Lancashire County Fire Brigade | Leigh |
| GJJ818 | 1.CU | C/Unit | 40 | 61 | LCC London Fire Brigade | Lambeth |
| CKG143 | | Foam/C | 40 | 66 | City of Cardiff | Cardiff Central |
| CKG178 | | HLL | 40 | 66 | City of Cardiff | Cardiff Central-1952 ET-1966 |
| GGK179 | | HLL | 40 | ? | Kent Fire Brigade | Chatham |
| GGN628 | | HLL | 41 | 51 | Essex County Fire Brigade | Walthemstow |
| GGN637 | | HLL | 41 | 56 | City of Liverpool | Mather Ave-Liverpool |
| GGN643 | | ET | 41 | 65 | Newcastle & Gateshead JFS | Pilgrim St-Newcastle |
| GGN648 | | HLL | 41 | 53 | Kent Fire Brigade | Maidstone |
| GGN696 | | HLL | 41 | ? | Middlesex Fire Brigade | Enfield |
| GGN706 | | HLL | 41 | ? | Middlesex Fire Brigade | Edmonton |
| GGN708 | | HLL | 41 | 48 | Essex County Fire Brigade | Barking |
| GGN834 | | HLL | 41 | ? | City of Liverpool | Banks Rd-Liverpool |
| GGN847 | | ET | 41 | 67 | Bournemouth Fire Brigade | Holdenhurst Rd-Bournemouth-1951-Pokesdown-1967 |
| GGN850 | | HLL | 41 | 55 | Northumberland Fire Brigade | Berwick |
| GGN854 | | HLL | 41 | 56 | City of Liverpool | Princes St-Liverpool-Lanc's CFB-1948 |
| GGN858 | | HLL | 41 | ? | Middlesex Fire Brigade | Kingsbury |
| GGU810 | | HLL | 41 | 59 | Lancashire County Fire Brigade | Newton le Willows |
| GGU813 | | HLL | 41 | 57 | LCC London Fire Brigade | A1 |
| GGU815 | | HLL | 41 | 65 | City of Plymouth | Crownhill-Plymouth |
| GGU824 | | HLL | 41 | ? | Kent Fire Brigade | Ramsgate |
| GGU827 | | HLL/FOT | 41 | 63 | City of Kingston upon Hull | Worship Rd-Hull Central |
| GGU828 | | HLL | 41 | 57 | Glamorgan County Fire Brigade | Bridgend |
| GGU831 | | HLL | 41 | 58 | City of Liverpool | Durning Rd-Liverpool |
| GGU839 | | HLL | 41 | 54 | Kent Fire Brigade | Folkestone |
| GGU876 | | FOT | 41 | ? | City of Liverpool | Hatton Gardens-Liverpool |
| GGU888 | | FOT | 41 | 58 | Lancashire County Fire Brigade | Eccles |
| GGX712 | | HLL | 41 | ? | Kent Fire Brigade | Gravesend |
| GGX714 | | HLL | 41 | 55 | Kent Fire Brigade | Sittingbourne |
| GGX726 | | HLL | 41 | 55 | Northumberland Fire Brigade | Alnwick |
| GGX975 | | FOT | 41 | ? | Kent Fire Brigade | Dartford |
| GGX983 | | FOT | 41 | 58 | Lancashire County Fire Brigade | Stretford |
| GGX990 | | FOT | 41 | 64 | City of Manchester | London Rd-Manchester -Withington Manchester |
| GGX993 | | FOT | 41 | 58 | Lancashire County Fire Brigade | Farnworth |
| GLE701 | | FOT | 41 | 68 | Newcastle & Gateshead JFS | |
| GLE725 | | ET | 41 | ? | Middlesex Fire Brigade | Acton |
| FYY328 | | HLL | 42 | ? | Middlesex Fire Brigade | Ealing/Heston |
| GLW30 | | FOT | 42 | 58 | Lancashire County Fire Brigade | Broughton |
| GLW301 | | FOT | 42 | 55 | North Riding of Yorkshire Fire Brigade | Hawes |
| GLW335 | | FOT | 42 | 66 | North Riding of Yorkshire Fire Brigade | Grangetown |
| GLW379 | | FOT | 42 | 58 | Glamorgan County Fire Brigade | Pontypridd |
| GLW381 | | FOT | 42 | 56 | Glamorgan County Fire Brigade | Whitchurch |
| GXM213 | | FOT | 43 | 54 | Kent Fire Brigade | Canterbury |
| GXM289 | | FOT | 43 | 53 | Kent Fire Brigade | Strood |
| GXM308 | | Foam/C | 43 | 59 | Glamorgan County Fire Brigade | Caerphilly-1953/Barry-1959 |
| GXM985 | | HLL/FOT | 43 | ? | Middlesex Fire Brigade | Hornsey |
| GXN259 | | HLL | 44 | ? | Lancashire County Fire Brigade | Huyton |
| GXN918 | | HLL | 44 | ? | | |
| GXN937 | | HLL | 44 | 66 | Durham County Fire Brigade | C24 Billingham-ET 1952-1960-FoT -1966 |

| GXN949 | | HLL | 44 | ? | Lancashire County Fire Brigade | Crosby |
|---|---|---|---|---|---|---|
| GXN974 | | HLL | 44 | 67 | Durham County Fire Brigade | Bishop Auckland/ B16 Hebburn ET 1952-1960-FoT-1967 |
| GXN979 | | FOT | 44 | ? | Wiltshire Fire Brigade | |
| GXN991 | | HLL | 44 | ? | East Sussex Fire Brigade | |
| GXT384 | | FOT | 44 | 55 | North Riding of Yorkshire Fire Brigade | Redcar /Whitby |

**The Newcastle City Fire Brigade operated EBB305, a Leyland TLM with a Metz 116' ladder. There were fifty-two German Metz ladders delivered to Britain before the hostilities of Second World War caused supplies to stop.  EBB305 was the thirty-seventh and was new in 1937. Of the type, this appliance was also one of only two Leyland TLM ladders fitted with a cab, the other example was DTB152 new to Morcambe & Heysham Fire Brigade in 1938**. *Ron Henderson*

# Leyland

| Reg No | Fleet No | TYPE | YR | OS | Appliance & Brigade Name | Details/Stations |
|--------|----------|------|-----|-----|--------------------------|------------------|
| | Metz-No MZ | | | | Leyland LM & TLM Metz Turntable Ladders | Metz Ladder Number |
| | | metre 26 27.4 30.5 45.7 | | | Height 85' 90' 100' 150' | **The earlier ladders were mounted on the LM chassis, but from late 1932 they were mounted on the TLM chassis. The TLM chassis was 4.4m (14.5ft) in length and was powered by either a 6 cylinder petrol or 8.5 litre Leyland diesel. The ladders were mostly 4 section, mechanically powered.** |
| N5951 | MZ-1 | TL | 24 | 41 | City of Manchester | London Road-Manchester-1940 St Mary's Gate-NFS Service-1941 **Destroyed by high explosive bomb-2 firemen killed** LM-Metz-85'L-Wooden |
| EK6489 | 31 MZ-2 | TL | 24 | 44 | Wigan County Borough FB | Chapel Lane-Wigan CBFB LM-Metz-85'L-Wooden |
| CX8400 | MZ-3 | TLP | 26 | ? | Huddersfield County Borough FB | Huddersfield Fire Station LM-Metz-82'L-Wooden-**400gpmP** |
| WH503 | MZ-4 | TL | 28 | 60 | Bolton County Borough FB | Marsden Rd-Bolton CBFB Ellen St-Nelson-Lancashire CFB-1960-**RTA Damaged-1954** LM-Metz-85'L-Wooden |
| DW5977 | MZ-5 | TL | 28 | 43 | Newport County Borough FB (Wales) | Newport Fire Stations-1940 / Ebbw Vale Fire Station-? **Monmouthshire / Period at Barry Fire Station- ?** LM-Metz-85'L-Wooden |
| TS7314 | MZ-6 | TL | 28 | 45 | Angus Area Fire Brigade (Scotland) | Central Fire Station-Dundee-1945 **Metz Ladders off N5951 transfered in Manchester-1945 Denbigh & Montgomeryshire** LM-Metz-85'L-Wooden |
| HL4010 | MZ-7 | TL | 28 | 47 | Wakefield County Borough FB | Wakefield Fire Station LM-Metz-85'L-Wooden |
| VP1999 | MZ-8 | TL | 28 | ? | City of Birmingham | Kings Norton-1930 / Pershore Rd South-Kings Norton LM-Metz-85'L-Wooden |
| CM8351 | MZ-9 | TL | 27 | 40 | Birkenhead County Borough FB | Whetstone Lane-Birkenhead LM-Metz-85'L-Wooden |
| KH7639 | MZ-10 | TL | 28 | 47 | City of Kingston upon Hull Fire Brigade | #1 Worship St-City of Kingston upon Hull FB-1933 #2 Southcoates Rd-City of Kingston upon Hull FB-1941 LM-Metz- 85'L-Wooden |
| WN1624 | MZ-11 | TL | 29 | 47 | Swansea County Borough FB (Wales) | **Swansea Fire Station-1940** / Guildhall St-Wrexham Bradley Rd-Wrexham-Denbighshire & Montgomery **Served a period at Cardiff- ?** LM-Metz-85'L-Wooden |
| OF1200 | MZ-12 | TL | 29 | ? | City of Birmingham | Ettington Rd-Aston LM-Metz-85'L-Wooden |
| RG1066 | MZ-13 | TL | 29 | 50 | North Eastern Area Fire Brigade (Scotland) | King St-Aberdeen-1950 **Ladder re-chassied onto Dennis F7 Chassis RSA999** Leyland Lynx-Metz-85'L-Wooden |
| UK9216 | MZ-14 | TL | 30 | 43 | Wolverhampton County Borough FB | Wolverhampton Fire Station-**Written off in RTA** LM-Metz-85'L-Wooden |
| TV3810 | MZ-15 | TLP | 31 | 55 | City of Nottingham | Shakespeare St-Nottingham LM-Metz-85'L-Wooden-**700gpmP** |
| DN2014 | MZ-16 | TL | 31 | 57 | City of York | Lower Friargate-York-1938 /Clifford St-York-1957 LM-Metz-85'L-Wooden |
| KF6683 | E3 MZ-17 | TL | 31 | 63 | City of Liverpool | 8 Mather Ave-Allerton-Liverpool LM-Metz-90'L-Wooden |

| Reg | Fleet | Type | No1 | No2 | Brigade | Details |
|---|---|---|---|---|---|---|
| FV3053 | MZ-18 | TL | 32 | 57 | Blackpool County Borough FB | Albert St-Blackpool-1948/South Shore-Blackpool-1955 Manchester Rd- Burnley CBFB-1957 LM-Metz-90'L-Wooden |
| VT9469 | MZ-19 | TLP | 33 | 57 | City of Stoke on Trent | Hanley-Stoke on Trent TLM2-Metz-90'L-Wooden-**500gpmP** |
| KV5800 | MZ-20 | TL | 33 | 61 | City of Coventry | Hales St-Coventry TLM2-Metz-90'L |
| RV4041 | MZ-21 | TLP | 33 | 62 | City of Portsmouth | Spring St-Portsmouth-1941 London Rd-Hilsea-Portsmouth-1957 Copnor Rd-Copnor-Portsmouth-1962 TLM2-Metz-98'L-**500gpmP** |
| KW6492 | MZ-22 | TL | 34 | 58 | City of Bradford | Nelson St-Bradford TLM2-Metz-101'L |
| WM9909 | MZ-23 | TL | 34 | 58 | Southport County Borough FB | Tulketh St-Southport-1938-Manchester Rd-Southport-1958 TLM2-Metz-90'L-Wooden |
| VD3307 | MZ-24 | TLP | 34 | 61 | Lanarkshire Fire Brigade (Scotland) | Hamilton Fire Station-Lanarkshire TLM2-Metz-90'L-**500gpmP** |
| DK9583 | No-4 MZ-25 | TLP | 34 | 57 | Rochdale County Borough FB | Maclure Rd-Rochdale TLM2-Metz-101'L-**500gpmP** |
| EN6080 | MZ-26 | TLP | 35 | 65 | Bury County Borough Fire Brigade | The Rock-Bury TLM2-Metz-98'L-**500gpmP** |
| RN7641 | MZ-27 | TL | 35 | 61 | Preston County Borough Fire Brigade | Tithebarn St-Preston TLM2-Metz-101'L |
| BU8888 | MZ-28 | TLP | 35 | 64 | Oldham County  Borough FB | #1 Ascroft St-Oldham CB-1948 #2 Werneth-Oldham CB-1964-**Preserved** TLM2-Metz-104'L-**500gpmP** |
| BOF389 | MZ-29 | TL | 35 | 61 | City of Birmingham | A01-Lancaster Gate-Birmingham-**Preserved in Birmingham** TLM2-Metz-104'L |
| AVB1 | TL1P-53TL MZ-30 | TLP | 36 | 68 | Croydon County Borough FB | Old St-Croydon-1963/Reserve-1968-London FB-**Preserved** TLM2-Metz-101'L-**500gpmP** |
| EMF535 | TL4 MZ-31 | TLP | 36 | 59 | Brentford & Chiswick Fire Brigade | London Rd-Isleworth-Middlesex-1948 London Rd-Isleworth-Middlesex FB-1959 TLM2-Metz-104'L-**500gpmP** |
| CKH407 | MZ-32 | TL | 36 | 59 | City of Kingston upon Hull FB | #1 Worship St-Hull Central-1950 #3 Analby Rd-old Hull West-1959 **Highest in the Country-Preserved** TLM2-Metz-150'L |
| EMX122 | TLP6 MZ-33 | TLP | 37 | 60 | Willesdon Fire Brigade | Pound Lane-Willesdon FB-1948 B36- Pound Lane-Willesdon-Middlesex FB-1960 **Destroyed in Fire 1964** TLM2-Metz-101'L-**500gpmP** |
| DGJ309 | TL21 MZ-34 | TLP | 37 | 64 | LCC London Fire Brigade | A5 Shaftsbury Ave-Soho-1964 **Damaged during the Blitz-1940- when Soho station was bombed  with station personnel killed/Preserved** TLM2-Metz-104'L-**500gpmP** |
| FMP411 | TLP1 MZ-35 | TLP | 37 | 59 | Hendon Fire Brigade | The Burroughs-Hendon FB-1948 B35 The Burroughs-Hendon-Middlesex FB -1959 TLM2-Metz-110'L-**500gpmP** |
| DKP476 | 190 MZ-36 | TLP | 37 | 61 | Kent Fire Brigade | D Div-Ladywell -Dover-Kent TLM2-Metz-104'L-**500gpmP** |
| EBB305 | MZ-37 | TLP | 37. | 61 | City of Newcastle Fire Brigade | A1 Pilgrim St-Newcastle-1948-Newcastle & Gateshead JFS **Turned over and written off during a drill. Limousine Cab** TLM2-Metz-116'L-**500gpmP** |
| EO7012 | MZ-38 | TLP | 37 | 65 | Barrow in Furrness County Borough FB | Abbey Rd-Barrow in Furrness TLM2-Metz-90'L-**500gpmP** |
| EKA342 | E-4 MZ-39 | TL | 38 | 58 | City of Liverpool | S1 Hatton Gardens-Liverpool-1946/ S6 Banks Rd-Liverpool-**Preserved** TLM2-Metz-104'L |
| DGJ310 | TL22 MZ-40 | TLP | 38 | 64 | LCC London Fire Brigade | B30-Commercial Rd-Whitechapel TLM2-Metz-104'L-**500gpmP** |

| | | | | | | |
|---|---|---|---|---|---|---|
| DTB152 | MZ-41 | TLP | 38 | 61 | Morcambe & Heysham Fire Brigade | Clarke St-Morcambe-1948<br>2.1 Clarke St-Morcambe-Lancashire CFB-1961<br>**Limousine Cab**<br>TLM2-Metz-101'L-**500gpmP** |
| DTB300 | MZ-42 | TLP | 38 | 61 | Lancashire County Fire Brigade | Manchester Rd-Accrington-1948<br>Manchester Rd-Accrington-1950<br>Ellen St-Nelson-1960/Reserve-1961<br>TLM2-Metz-101'L-**500gpmP** |
| GHK929 | MZ-43 | TLP | 38 | 65 | Essex County Fire Brigade | A9-Old Rd-Clacton-Essex CFB<br>**Sold Blackpool Pleasure Beach**<br>TLM2-Metz-101'L-**500gpmP** |
| VV7200 | MZ-44 | TLP | 38 | 67 | Northamptonshire Fire Brigade | The Mounts-Northampton-1967<br>TLM2-Metz-104'L-**500gpmP** |
| BFH972 | TL-3<br>MZ-45 | TLP | 38 | 68 | City of Gloucester | Bearland-Gloucester-1956<br>Eastern Ave-Gloucester-1968-**Preserved**<br>TLM2-Metz-101'L-**700gpmP** |
| EKC982 | E-5<br>MZ-46 | TL | 38 | 60 | City of Liverpool | S1 Hatton Gardens-Liverpool-1954<br>S8 Mather Ave-Allerton-Liverpool- 1960-**Preserved**<br>TLM2-Metz-104'L |
| FMA210 | MZ-47 | TLP | 38 | 71 | Macclesfield County Borough FB | Chester Rd-Macclesfield-1967<br>Macon Way-Macclesfield-1971 -**Preserved**<br>TLM2-Metz-104'L-**500gpmP** |
| FGU691 | TL26<br>MZ-48 | TLP | 39 | 64 | LCC London Fire Brigade | D61-Albert Embankment-Lambeth- 1964<br>TLM2-Metz-101'L-**700gpmP** |
| EDV499 | MZ-49 | TLP | 39 | 65 | Torquay County Borough FB | Market St-Torquay-Devon<br>TLM2-Metz-104'L-**500gpmP** |
| FGU692 | TL27<br>MZ-50 | TLP | 39 | 64 | LCC London Fire Brigade | D71-Este Rd-Battersea-1964<br>TLM2-Metz-101'L-**700gpmP** |
| ETC4 | MZ-51 | TL | 39 | 61 | Stretford & Urmston Joint Fire Brigade | Park Rd-Stretford-1948<br>Park Rd-Stretford-1961-Lancashire CFB<br>TLM2-Metz-104'L |
| BDY507 | MZ-52 | TLP | 39 | 68 | Hastings County Borough FB | Bohemia Rd-Hastings-East Sussex<br>TLM2-Metz-101'L-**500gpmP** |

London operated German-built Metz turntable ladders on four of its Leyland chassis. FGU692 is one example, seen at Battersea, that served almost twenty-five years, and was one of a pair delivered to the capital with 30 metre (101ft) ladders. Similar appliance, DGJ309, is preserved in the south of England and is regularly seen at rallies and occasionally at the Royal Tournament.
*Keith Wardell collection*

| | Merryweather Ladder-MW | | | | Leyland LM & TLM Chassied Turntable Ladders | The earlier ladders were mounted on the LM chassis, which was replaced by the TLM chassis in late 1932. The chassis was 4.4m(14.5 ft) in length and was powered by a 6 cylinder petrol or 8.6 litre leyland diesel. The ladders were mostly 4 section 100ft mechanically driven. |
|---|---|---|---|---|---|---|
| JBB853 NFS order | MW-43 | TL | 40 | 66 | City of Newcastle Fire Brigade | A1 Pilgrim St-Newcastle-1948/B1-Gateshead-N&G JFS-1966          TLM2-Merryweather-100'L |
| GKA983 NFS order | E-6 MW-44 | TLP | 40 | 67 | City of Liverpool | #2 Essex St-Liverpool-1958 #2Belvidere Rd-Liverpool-1967 -Preserved TLM2-Merryweather-100 L |
| DGE80 NFS order | MW-45 | TL | 40 | ? | Glasgow Fire Service | Glasgow Fire Stations TLM2-Merryweather-100 L |
| GHW415 NFS order | MW-46 | TL | 40 | 68 | City of Bristol | Silver St-City of Bristol FB-1947 3-1 Salisbury-Wiltshire FB-1968/Preserved in Bristol TLM2-Merryweather-100'L |
| GNC800 NFS order | MW-47 | TL | 40 | 71 | City of Manchester | London Rd-Manchester-1950 Wilmslow Rd Withington-Manchester-1959 Brownley Rd-Wythenshawe- 1971 / Preserved TLM2-Merryweather-100'L |
| DSF140 NFS order | MW-48 | TL | 40 | 54 | Edingburgh Fire Brigade (Scotland) | Lauriston Place-Edingburgh-1948 Lauriston Place-Edingburgh-1954/ South Eastern Area FB Ladders re-chassied onto AEC Regent-JFS372 TLM2-Merryweather-100'L |
| GWJ649 NFS order | MW-49 | TL | 40 | 62 | City of Sheffield | #4Mansfield Rd-Sheffield TLM2-Merryweather-100 L |
| DKW755 NFS order | MW-56 | TL | 41 | 59 | City of Bradford | Nelson St-Bradford TLM2-Merryweather-100 L |
| EVC919 NFS order | MW-57 | TL | 41 | 57 | City of Coventry | Canley-Coventry CFB-1948/Chapel Lane-Wigan CBFB-1957 TLM2-Merryweather-100'L |
| BRJ333 NFS order | MW-58 | TL | 41 | 61 | City of Salford | The Crescent-Salford Preserved at Manchester Museum of Transport TLM2-Merryweather-100'L |

During the war the National Fire Service received batches of Turntable Ladders from several suppliers. GLW418, a 1942 Leyland TD7 with 100 foot ladders, was one of a batch of 27 and was delivered to Bethel Street in the City of Norwich, but later went on to serve at Princes Street station of the Suffolk and Ipswich Fire Service after the war. It was replaced by an AEC Mercury / Merryweather in 1966.
*Keith Wardell collection*

| | MW-No | | | | | |
|---|---|---|---|---|---|---|
| YJ7700<br>NFS order | MW-59 | TL | 41 | 62 | Angus Area Fire Brigade<br>(Scotland) | West Bell St-Central Dundee<br>TLM2-Merryweather |
| JNW954<br>NFS order | MW-60 | TL | 41 | ? | Leeds City Fire Brigade | ?<br>TLM2-Merryweather 100 L |
| GKH156<br>NFS order | MW-61 | TL | 41 | 62 | City of Kingston upon Hull FB | #2 Southcoates Rd-Hull East-1950/ **Selby Fire Station-?**<br>Dewsbury-West Riding of Yorkshire FB<br>TLM2-Merryweather-100'L |
| XS5454<br>NFS order | MW-62 | TL | 41 | 61 | Western Area Fire Brigade<br>(Scotland) | Johnstone St-Paisley-Western AFB<br>TLM2-Merryweather-100'L |
| XG7767<br>NFS order | MW-63 | TL | 41 | 62 | Middlesbrough County Borough FB | S1 Park Rd South-Middlesbrough- 1962/Reserve-1968<br>**Sold to Merryweather as a loan TL**<br>TLM2-Merryweather-100'L |
| BG6246<br>NFS order | MW-103 | TL | **40 ?**<br>43 | 59 | Birkenhead County Borough FB | Whetstone Lane-Charing Cross- Birkenhead<br>TLM2-Merryweather-100'L |

| | MW-No | | | | **Leyland TD7**<br>**Chassied Turntable Ladders** | These appliances were ordered by the War Department and supplied to the newly formed NFS. The ladders were mounted on the TD bus chassis while the driver sat alongside the 8.6 litre engine in a half cab. The four section 100 ft Merryweather ladder was powered by the engine. |
|---|---|---|---|---|---|---|
| | | | | | **War Service** | **Station & Fire Brigade** |
| 10863 RN | | TLP | 41 | ? | **Royal Navy** | **Portsmouth Dockyard-Royal Navy**<br>Merryweather 100 L |
| EDR706 | MW-71A | TLP | 42 | 67 | **Royal Navy** | **Devonport Dockyard-Royal Navy-1946**<br>WD48 Camels Head-Plymouth-1967 |
| GLW405<br>NFS order | MW-68 | TL | 42 | 59 | North East<br>(Newcastle upon Tyne) | Dun Cow St-City of Sunderland FB<br>**Sold to Rentokil Ltd** |
| FZ9326<br>NFS order | MW-69 | TL | 42 | ? | Belfast Fire Brigade | Station Unknown- |
| GLW406<br>NFS order | MW-70 | TL | 42 | 58 | Oldham<br>(North West) | Astcroft St-Oldham CBFB-1946<br>Corporation St-Hyde-Cheshire FB-1958 |
| GLW407<br>NFS order | MW-71 | TL | 42 | 66 | Merseyside | 5 Westminster Rd-Liverpool FB-1962 Reserve-1966 |
| GLW408<br>NFS order | MW-72 | TL | 42 | 63 | Bedfordshire | Church St-Luton CBFB-1948/ Wippendell Rd-Watford-1956<br>Barkers Lane-Bedford-Bedfordshire FB-1963 |
| GLW410<br>NFS order | MW-73 | TL | 42 | 60 | Lothian & Borders<br>(Edingburgh) | King St-Aberdeen-North Eastern Area FB<br>**Fitted with cab/Federal Ind-Preserved in NFS colours** |
| GLW411<br>NFS order | MW-75 | TL | 42 | 84 | Lanarkshire | A7 North West-Glasgow-Glasgow FS-1968<br>**Swapped in 1968 for a 1928 Albion Pump from Galway.** |
| GLW412<br>NFS order | MW-76 | TL | 42 | 62 | Huddersfield<br>(Yorkshire) | Huddersfield Fire Station<br>Huddersfield County Borough FB |
| GLW413<br>NFS order | MW-77 | TL | 42 | 64 | Norfolk | Bethel St-City of Norwich FB-1948<br>B17 Brentwood-Essex CFB-1962<br>B27 Basildon-Essex CFB-1964 |
| GLW414<br>NFS order | MW-78 | TL | 42 | 66 | Derbyshire | Derby Fire Station's-1945 / Kettering Fire Station-1958<br>The Headlands-Kettering-Northamptonshire FB-1966 |
| GLW415<br>NFS order | MW-79 | TLP | 42 | 68 | Willesdon<br>(London) | Pound Lane-Willesdon-1945<br>D63 Dockhead-LCC London FB-1948<br>Albert Rd-Blackpool CBFB-1964/ Res-1968/ **Scrapped 1992** |
| GLW416<br>NFS order | MW-80 | TL | 42 | 64 | North East | Newcastle City Fire Station's-1945<br>Kepple St-South Shields-South Shields CB |
| GLW417<br>NFS order | MW-81 | TL | 42 | 65 | Merseyside | 9 Longmoor Lane-Fazakerly-Liverpool FB |
| GLW418<br>NFS order | MW-82 | TLP | 42 | 66 | Norfolk | Bethel St-City of Norwich FB-1948<br>Princes St-Ipswich-1965-Suffolk & Ipswich FS |
| FZ9776<br>NFS order | MW-83 | TL | 42 | ? | Belfast Fire Brigade | Central Station Belfast-1957 |

| | | | | | | | |
|---|---|---|---|---|---|---|---|
| **GLW419**<br>NFS order | **MW-84** | TL | 42 | 67 | Lincolnshire | Lincoln Fire Station -A1 South Park Ave-City of Lincoln |
| **GLW420**<br>NFS order | **MW-85** | TL | 42 | 59 | Berkshire & Reading | B1 Caversham Rd-Berkshire&Reading FB<br>**Ladder Re-chassied onto AEC Mercury PRX62** |
| **GLW421**<br>NFS order | **MW-86** | TL | 42 | 67 | North East | Park Rd South-Middlesborough FB-1948<br>Loan period at Barrow in Furrness CB<br>Marsden Rd-Bolton CBFB-1966-Reserve-1967 |
| **GLW422**<br>NFS order | **MW-87** | TL | 42 | 60 | Birmingham | A1 Lancaster Circus-City of Birmingham FB-1948<br>Wolverhampton CBFB-1960<br>Sold to Cape Hill Breweries-Smethwick/**Preserved** |
| **GLW423**<br>NFS order | **MW-88** | TLP | 42 | 58 | South East | B Div New Rd-Chatham-Kent Fire Brigade |
| **GLW425**<br>NFS order | **MW-90** | TL | 42 | 68 | Croydon<br>(London) | Old Town-Croydon CBFB-1943<br>Greenock Renfrewshire-Western Area NFS Region-1948<br>Greenock-Western Area FB-1968/**Preserved** |
| **GLW426**<br>NFS order | **MW-91** | TLP | 42 | 61 | Manchester | London Rd-City of Manchester FB |
| **GLW427**<br>NFS order | **MW-92** | TL | 42 | 74 | Humberside | #2 South Coates Rd-Hull East-1964<br>#3 Calvert Rd-Hull West-1974<br>City of Kingston upon Hull FB |
| **GLW428**<br>NFS order | **MW-93** | TL | 42 | 68 | Worcestershire | Copenhagen St-Worcester City&County FB-1968<br>**Sold to Rentokil Ltd** |
| **GLW429**<br>NFS order | **MW-94** | TL | 42 | 64 | Glamorgan | Alexandra Rd-Swansea CBFB-1956<br>Grove Place-Swansea CBFB-1964 |
| **GLW430**<br>NFS order | **MW-95** | TL | 42 | 63 | Greater Manchester | King St-Stockport CBFB-1948<br>Heathside-Warrington CBFB-1963 |
| **GLW431**<br>NFS order | **MW-96** | TL | 42 | 62 | Wolverhampton | **Wolverhampton CB Station-?** / Rolfe St-Smethwick-1945<br>Walsall Fire Station-Walsall County Borough FB |

| | | | | | **Leyland TSC18 Forward Control Beaver-Chassied Turntable Ladders** | **The Beaver chassis was chosen for a large order of TL's placed by the War Department which when built were supplied to the newly formed NFS. Most of them came supplied with 500gpm pumps. The Beaver TSC18 was a 7 ton chassis dating from before the war. It was powered by a Gardner 5 litre diesel.** |
|---|---|---|---|---|---|---|
| | | | | | **War Service** | **Station & Fire Brigade** |
| **GXA61**<br>NFS order | **MW-97** | TL | 43 | 63 | Leicestershire | Swindon Fire Station-1945<br>**Transfered Smethwick &West Bromwich CB**<br>Rolfe St-Smethwick-? Hargate St-West Bromwich-1963 |
| **GXA62**<br>NFS order | **MW-104** | TLP | 43 | 72 | Weymouth<br>(Dorset) | North Quay-Weymouth CBFB-1948<br>A7 North Quay-Weymouth-Dorset FB- 1972 |
| **GXA63**<br>NFS order | **MW-105** | TL | 43 | 64 | Rugby<br>(Warwickshire) | N26 Rugby Fire Station-1948<br>Castle St-Kidderminster-Worcester City & CFB-1964 |
| **GXA64**<br>NFS order | **MW-106** | TL | 43 | 66 | Blackburn<br>(Lancashire) | B71 Byrom Rd-Blackburn County Borough FB-1966<br>**Preserved** |
| **GXA65**<br>NFS order | **MW-107** | TLP | 43 | ? | Northampton | Kettering Fire Station-1945/ **Harrogate Area- ?**<br>**Leeds City Fire Stations- ?** |
| **GXA66**<br>NFS order | **MW-108** | TLP | 43 | ? | Glasgow | Station unknown-Glasgow Fire Service<br>**Sold to Thomas Nichol-Demolition Specialist-Kirkcaldy** |
| **GXA67**<br>NFS order | **MW-109** | TLP | 43 | 68 | North Riding of Yorkshire | North Marine Drive-Scarborough<br>North Riding of Yorkshire FB-1968 |
| **GXA68**<br>NFS order | **MW-110** | TLP | 43 | 62 | Maidstone<br>(Kent) | C Div-Market Place-Maidstone-Kent Fire Brigade |
| **GXA69**<br>NFS order | **MW-111** | TLP | 43 | 65 | Exeter<br>(Devon) | #1 Howell Rd-Exeter -1968 -Devon Fire Brigade |
| **GXA70**<br>NFS order | **MW-112** | TLP | 43 | 59 | Chesterfield<br>(Derbyshire) | C01-New Beetwell St-Chesterfield -Derbyshire Fire Service |
| **GZ1445**<br>NFS order | **MW-113** | TLP | 43 | ? | Belfast<br>(Northern Ireland) | **Fire Station Unknown-Belfast Fire Brigade** |

| | | | | | | |
|---|---|---|---|---|---|---|
| GXA71<br>NFS order | MW-114 | TLP | 43 | 72 | Cosham<br>(Portsmouth) | #3 High St-Cosham-City of Portsmouth 1946<br>B28 Porchester-1947<br>Brunswick St-Wakefield CBFB-1972-**Derelict Leeds 1982** |
| GXA72<br>NFS order | MW-115 | TLP | 43 | 72 | Southampton<br>(Hampshire) | D54-St Mary's Rd-City of Southampton -1947<br>B18 Wimborne Rd-Poole-Dorset FB-1972 |
| GXA73<br>NFS order | MW-116 | TLP | 43 | 63 | Doncaster<br>(Yorkshire) | Ledger Way-Doncaster-Doncaster County Borough FB-1963 |
| GXA74<br>NFS order | MW-117 | TLP | 43 | 64 | Yeovil<br>(Somerset) | **Yeovil - ?/ City of Bristol - ? /**<br>Lansdowne Rd-Cheltenham FB-1960<br>12 Keynsham Rd-Cheltenham-Gloucestershire FS-1964 |
| GXA75<br>NFS order | MW-118 | TLP | 43 | 66 | Tynemouth<br>(North East) | Norfolk St-Tynemouth-Tynemouth CBFB-1959<br>Preston Nth Rd-Tynemouth CBFB-1966<br>**Sold Rentokil Ltd-1972/Derelict-1976** |
| GXA76<br>NFS order | 20-A TL2<br>MW-119 | TLP | 43 | 71 | Newport<br>(South Wales) | B09 Malpas Newport CBFB-1966<br>Westgate Street-Cardiff City FB-1967<br>Llandrindod Wells-Brecon & Radnor FB-1971<br>Derelict, Irlam '82 |
| GXA77<br>NFS order | MW-120 | TLP | 43 | 60 | Grays<br>(Essex) | C50 Grays-Essex County FB-1948<br>B30- 87 London Rd-Southend Southend CBFB-1960 |
| GXA79<br>NFS order | MW-121 | TLP | 43 | 73 | Rhyl<br>(Flintshire) | W1 Coast Rd-Rhyl-Flintshire CFB-1948<br>Westgate St-Cardiff City FB-1967<br>Whitchurch-Cardiff City FB-1973 |
| GXA80<br>NFS order | MW-122 | TLP | 43 | ? | Edinburgh<br>(South Eastern) | **Edinburgh Fire Stations - 1946**<br>**West Bell St-Dundee-Angus Area FB- ?** |
| GXA83<br>NFS order | MW-123 | TLP | 43 | 62 | Dudley<br>(Midlands) | Tower St-Dudley-Dudley County Borough |
| GXA85<br>NFS order | 30-B TL1<br>MW-124 | TLP | 43 | 62 | Dartford<br>(Kent) | B Div Overy St-Dartford -Kent Fire Brigade |
| GXA86<br>NFS order | MW-125 | TLP | 43 | 68 | Ebbw Vale<br>(Monmouthshire) | **Ebbw Vale-Monmouthshire CFB- ?**<br>01Malpas-Newport CB-1966<br>02-Maindee-Newport CBFB-1968 |
| GXA88<br>NFS order | MW-126 | TLP | 43 | 65 | Rotherham<br>(Yorkshire) | Erskine Rd-Rotherham-Rotherham County Borough FB |
| GXA90<br>NFS order | MW-132 | TLP | 43 | 66 | Grimsby<br>(Hull) | C1Peakes Lane-Grimsby-Grimsby CBFB-1953<br>Barnard St-West Hartlepool-Hartlepool CB-1959<br>Stranton-West Hartlepool CBFB-1966 |

There were twenty-one Leyland Beaver TSC chassied Turntable Ladders delivered to the National Fire Service in 1943. GXA72 is shown here and these carried Merryweather 30.3 metre (100') ladders. Many of this type of machine were sold to firms involved in high rise building renovation and tree surgery.
*Keith Wardell ollection*

Photographed outside the old Borough Road fire station in Darlington County Borough days, 999MHN is an example of the Leyland Firemaster Turntable Ladder and was the first of a batch of ten machines. Delivered in 1959, it was fitted with David Haydon bodywork and Magirus ladders, and was the only one which did not have a built in fire pump. It was also one of two appliances built on the Leyland TFM2 coach chassis, the other turntable ladder, 9990DA, was delivered to Wolverhampton County Borough. *Ian Moore*

| Types Beaver Comet Firemaster Leyland-Daf | | | | | | Leyland Chassied Turntable Ladders | The Leyland Comet chassis which was powered by a 5.76 litre diesel engine had the unusual Dutch Geesink ladder mounted. West Riding was the only UK Brigade to purchase it. The Beaver chassis had an updated cab with a different appearance than the NFS issue Beavers. They also were fitted with 500gpm pumps. They were powered by a Leyland 9.8litre diesel |
|---|---|---|---|---|---|---|---|
| | | | | | | | Leyland Beavers were also purchased by Hong Kong. |
| KWU140 | | | TL | 51 | 67 | West Riding of Yorkshire Fire Brigade | Albert Rd-Harrogate-1966/Skipton Rd-Harrogate-1967 Leyland Comet-Geesink-107'L |
| KWU305 | | | TL | 51 | 64 | West Riding of Yorkshire Fire Brigade | Batley Fire Station Leyland Comet-Geesink-107'L |
| OZ8300 | | | TLP | 54 | ? | Northern Ireland Fire Brigade | Londonderry Fire Station Leyland Beaver-Morris-Magirus-100'L |
| NWR249 | | | TLP | 54 | 69 | West Riding of Yorkshire Fire Brigade | Keighley Fire Station /Preserved Leyland Beaver-Morris-Magirus-100'L |
| NWR250 | | | TLP | 54 | 67 | West Riding of Yorkshire Fire Brigade | Hightown Rd-Cleckheaton Leyland Beaver-Morris-Magirus-100'L |
| 999MHN | 4 1 191 | | TL | 59 | 83 | Darlington County Borough FB | Borough Rd-Darlington-1972 / St Cuthbert's Way-Darlington Durham County Fire Brigade Preserved National Museum Trust Firemaster-Haydon-Magirus DL30 |
| 9990DA | | | TLP | 60 | 78 | Wolverhampton County Borough Fire Brigade | E05 Wolverhampton-1967 E06 Fallings Park-1974/Reserve-1978/West Midlands FS Firemaster-Haydon/Carmichael-Magirus DL30 |
| G774GFR | | | TL | 90 | | Lancashire County Fire Brigade | BD90 Belvedere Rd-Burnley DAF 1900-Angloco-Metz DLK30 |

| | | | | | | Leyland Chassied Hydraulic Platforms | |
|---|---|---|---|---|---|---|---|
| AHG1B | 279 | | PHP ET | 63 | 76 | Burnley County Borough FB | Manchester Rd-Burnley-1965 Belvidere Rd-Burnley-1974 E90 Burnley-1976/Lancashire County FB Comet-John Morris-Simon DS50 |
| HCO999F | | | HP | 67 | 82 | City of Plymouth | Ferndale Rd-Camels Head-1974 W48 Camels Head-1982-Devon CFB Booms Re-ch onto S & Drewry WY/Benson-VDV144X Beaver-Carmichael-Simon SS65 |
| YDJ278H | 1090 | | HP | 70 | 84 | St Helens County Borough FB | Parr Stocks Rd-St Helens-1974/E1-Merseyside FB-1984 Beaver-Carmichael-Orbitor 72' |
| PAK247H re reg PKW968J | | | HP | 70 | 78 | City of Bradford | Nelson St-1974 Nelson St-1976/Training School-1979 West Yorkshire FS Mastiff-Carmichael-Orbitor 50' |
| HHB247K | | | HP | 72 | 82 | Merthyr Tydfil County Borough FB (Wales) | Dynevor St-1974 21 Dynevor St-Merthyr-1982-Mid Glamorgan CFS Beaver-Carmichael-Orbitor 72' |
| GPX70N | | | HP | 74 | 88 | Hampshire Fire Service | A1 Ordnance Rd Aldershot-1988 Booms Re-chassied onto Dodge G16C/Saxon-G186UPO Beaver-HCB Angus-Simon SS70 |
| G504XFH | 700 | | ALP | 90 | | Gloucestershire Fire & Rescue Service | 12 Keynsham Rd-Cheltenham Daf 2500 FAS-Angloco-Bronto 28-2TI |

| | | | | 58 | 63 | Leyland Firemaster Chassied Series | The series spanned only 5 years, 1958-1963 with 10 examples being built. It was mounted on a coach chassis with a mid ship's mounted 9.8 litre Leyland C1 engine .Only 2 examples were TL's. They were mounted on the TFM2 chassis. All were fitted with front mounted 350/500gpm pumps with the exception of 999MHN. |
|---|---|---|---|---|---|---|---|
| 999MHN | 4 1 / 191 | | TL | 59 | 83 | Darlington County Borough FB | Borough Rd-Darlington-1974-Durham County FB Preserved National Museum Trust -Haydon-Magirus |

| | | | | | | |
|---|---|---|---|---|---|---|
| WXJ286 | | PE | 59 | 72 | City of  Manchester | London Road-1972<br>Bodywork-Cocker |
| YGG209 | | PE | 59 | 78 | Glasgow Fire Service<br>(Scotland) | B1 South-1975 /B1 South-Strathclyde FB-1978/**Preserved**<br>Bodywork-Haydon |
| 74CGD | | PE | 60 | 78 | Glasgow Fire Service<br>(Scotland) | C1 North West-1975<br>A4 Kelbourne St-North West-Strathclyde FB 1978<br>Bodywork-Cocker |
| 9990DA | | TLP | 60 | 78 | Wolverhampton County Borough FB | E05 Wolverhampton-1967<br>E06 Fallings Park-Wolverhampton-West Midlands FS-1974<br>Reserve-197-**Originally fitted with a 100' Magirus ladder licence built by David Haydon, Birmingham**<br>Wilsdon-Haydon/Magirus-100'L |
| 7596N | | PE | 60 | 72 | City of  Manchester | London Road-1972<br>Bodywork-Cocker |
| 6461ND | | ET | 62 | 75 | City of  Manchester | London Road-1975 -**Preserved**<br>Bodywork-Smiths |
| 6900NF | | PE | 63 | 75 | City of  Manchester | Ash Street-1967 -E51 Blackley-Manchester-1974<br>Bodywork-Cocker |
| 863YPU | | P/EST | 63 | 73 | Essex County Fire Brigade | A10 Cowdray Ave-Colchester-1965<br>A11Fronks Rd-Dovercourt-1973<br>Bodywork-Haydon |
| 864YPU | | P/EST | 63 | 74 | Essex County Fire Brigade | C50 Hogg Lane-Grays-1969/C55 Civic Square-Tilbury-1974<br>Bodywork-Haydon |

| | | | | | Leyland  Chassied<br>Emergency/Rescue Tenders | |
|---|---|---|---|---|---|---|
| FV9696 | | ET | 32 | ? | Blackpool County Borough<br>Fire Brigade | Albert Rd-Blackpool<br>FK-Limousine |
| EMX121 | | ET | 36 | 58 | Willesdon Fire Brigade | 34B19-London Rd-Isleworth-1948   34B12<br>G30 Harrow Rd-Wembley-1957-Middlesex F&AS-**ET2**<br>FK6-Cub-Limousine |
| CBY1 | | Pump<br>Salv/T | 37 | 63 | Croydon County Borough<br>Fire Brigade | 38C1-Croydon Fire Station-Old Town-Croydon-1963<br>FK9-Cub-Limousine |

A working shot of the short-lived Leyland Firemaster 863YPU, a Pump/Salvage tender with Haydon bodywork, that was delivered in 1963 to Colchester.  A similar appliance went to Grays in Essex County at the same time. It is unfortunate that more of the 'Firemaster's' did not find their way into the hands of the preservationist.
*Keith Wardell collection*

| Reg | Fleet | Type | | | Brigade | Details |
|---|---|---|---|---|---|---|
| ACL737 | | Pump/ET Salv/T | 37 | 63 | City of Norwich | 13A12 Bethel St-Norwich -A Div-Bethel St-Norwich FK9-Cub-Limousine |
| EOJ877 | | ET/CAV | 38 | ? | City of Birmingham | A1 Lancaster Place-Central -**Green livery** SKZ5-Cub-Limousine |
| BGG305 | | ET | 38 | 64 | Glasgow Fire Service (Scotland) | SKZ5-Cub-Limousine |
| ETC5 | | ET/CU | 39 | 62 | Stretford & Urmston Fire Brigade | 27E12 Park Rd-Stretford-1947 D60 Stretford-Lancashire County FS DZ1-Saloon |
| BDY509 | | Pump/ET Salv/T | 39 | 68 | Hastings County Borough Fire Brigade | 31D12 Bohemia Rd-Hastings-**Preserved** FK9-Cub-Limousine |
| BFR700 | | Pump Salv/T | 39 | 60 | Blackpool County Borough Fire Brigade | 29C12-Albert Rd-Blackpool -**Preserved** TLM-Limousine-Burlingham |
| LME979 | | Pump/ET | 40 | 60 | Tottenham Fire Brigade | 36B13 The Green-Tottenham A7 Tottenham-Middlesex F&AS-1960 SKZ5-Cub-Limousine |
| AHE999K | | ET | 71 | 85 | Barnsley County Borough Fire Brigade | A1 Broadside-Barnsley-1974 A1 Barnsley-South Yorkshire CFS Super Comet-HCB Angus |
| EAU999L | | ET | 72 | 82 | City of Nottingham | #1 Shakespeare St-Nottingham-1974 B18 Shakespeare St-Central-1982-Nottinghamshire FB Mastiff-HCB Angus |
| NJC789M | | ET | 73 | 81 | Caernarfonshire Fire Service (Wales) | Beach Rd-Bangor-1974 Beach Rd-Bangor-1981 Lanberis Rd-Caernarfon-Gwynedd Fire Service **Converted Chemical Incident Unit ;** Terrier- |
| D96DST | | ET | 86 | | Highlands & Islands Fire Brigade (Scotland) | A1 Harbour Rd-Inverness Sherpa 300-F&Wylie |
| GDZ2146 | | ESU | 89 | | Northern Ireland Fire Brigade | C06 Cecil St-Newry Sherpa 300-Alexander |
| GDZ2147 | | ESU | 89 | | Northern Ireland Fire Brigade | B09 Portferry Rd-Newtownards Sherpa 300-Alexander |
| GDZ2148 | | ESU | 89 | | Northern Ireland Fire Brigade | E04 Agnew Rd-Larne Sherpa 300-Alexander |
| G505XFH | 702 | ESU | 90 | | Gloucestershire Fire & Rescue Service | 05 Eastern Ave-Gloucester-**HIAB 071 Crane fitted** Daf 17-18-Rosenbaur |
| J250PJA | | ET Salv/T | 92 | | Greater Manchester County Fire Service | **ex C30 Maclure Rd-Rochdale-1994/** Reserve-Daf Roadrunner 10.15-Nova Scotia |
| L949EFV | 30001 | ISU | 94 | | Lancashire County Fire Brigade | A11 Cable St-Lancaster (**Reserve**) Daf T45-Fosters Commercials |
| L950EFV | 30002 | ISU | 94 | | Lancashire County Fire Brigade | B70 Manchester Rd-Accrington Daf T45-Fosters Commercials |
| L951EFV | 30003 | ISU | 94 | | Lancashire County Fire Brigade | A11 Cable St-Lancaster Daf T45-Fosters Commercials |
| L952EFV | 30004 | ISU | 94 | | Lancashire County Fire Brigade | C54 Welbank Rd-Chorley Daf T45-Fosters Commercials |
| L953EFV | 30005 | ISU | 94 | | Lancashire County Fire Brigade | 37 St Annes Rd-South Shore-Blackpool Daf T45-Fosters Comercials |
| L978ENC | | ET Salv/T | 94 | | Greater Manchester County Fire Service | A13 Liverpool Rd-Eccles Daf 45-160-Bedwas/Pickering |
| L979ENC | | ET Salv/T | 94 | | Greater Manchester County Fire Service | E53 Birch St-Gorton Daf 45-160-Bedwas/Pickering |
| L980ENC | | ET Salv/T | 94 | | Greater Manchester County Fire Service | D42 Lisburne Lane-Offerton Daf 45-160-Bedwas/Pickering |
| L981ENC | | ET Salv/T | 94 | | Greater Manchester County Fire Service | B24 Robin Park Rd-Wigan Daf 45-160-Bedwas/Pickering |
| M364SDB | | ET Salv/T | 94 | | Greater Manchester County Fire Service | C30 Maclure Rd-Rochdale Daf 45-160-Whiteacre-Bedwas |

Traditionally, many of the larger cities operated large Emergency Tenders. Nottingham was one as illustrated by EAU999L, a Leyland Mastiff with HCB Angus bodywork. Delivered in 1972 it served at central fire station in Shakespeare Street for ten years before being replaced by a smaller Dodge S-series machine. Though this small ET was replaced by a larger Dodge G13C Chassis model in 1988. Shown in the picture is the 'infamous county motif' which was later replaced on the appliances at the request of Fire-fighters. *Michael Lawmon*

| Chassis<br>Cub<br>Comet 70<br>Comet 90<br>Laird<br>Boxer<br>Terrier<br>Mastiff | | | | | **Leyland Chassied<br>Specialist Appliances**<br><br>**Weight**<br>**3 Tons**<br>**6 Tons**<br>**7.5 Tons**<br>**7 to 16 Tons**<br>**10 to 16 Tons**<br>**6.5 to 9.5 Tons**<br>**16 to 24 Tons** | **British Leyland over the years has swallowed up many companies over the years including Albion in 1951 Scammell in 1955, AEC in 1962 and in 1968 merged with BMC. Many names of types synonymous with former companies lived on under Leyland ie Claymore and Clydesdale . Many other types were renamed as in the BMC FJ which became the Laird then the Boxer then the Freighter. In 1987 Leyland was taken over by DAF vehicles.** |
|---|---|---|---|---|---|---|
| **XG3910** | | Light Unit | 36 | 66 | Middlesbrough Fire Brigade | ex Pump/E Middlesbrough-1959<br>Park Rd South-Middlesbrough-1966<br>FT3A-MFB |
| **CLX543** | | Welfare Unit | 37 | ? | LCC London Fire Brigade | D61 Embankment-Lambeth/**Welfare Coach-now preserved**<br>Cub- |
| **CLX544** | CU-2 | C/Unit | 37 | 59 | LCC London Fire Brigade | D61 Embankment-Lambeth-1953-59<br>Cub- |
| **FKA844** | | FOT | 38 | 66 | City of Liverpool | Liverpool City Airport (Speke) -**6x4 WD**<br>KZD-LFB |
| **FKO306** | | P/FoT | 39 | 53 | Kent Fire Brigade | B35 Wrotham Rd-Gravesend<br>Tiger FKT- |
| **GYO596** | **100** | Rec/V | 45 | 57 | City of Birmingham | A1 Lancaster Circus-Central |
| **GYO880** | | Rec/V | 45 | 68 | Glamorgan Fire Service (Wales) | B1 Bridgend Fire Station-1964 /B1 Sunnyside-Bridgend-1968    **3 Axle Wrecker** |
| **KWD395** | | BL/ET | 51 | 62 | Warwick County Fire Brigade | ?    **- Sold D Hick's Recovery-Rowborough-Glouc's**<br>Leyland **6x6 chassis** |
| **JTG914** | | Rec/V | 51 | ? | Glamorgan Fire Service (Wales) | Brigade Workshops |
| **DLK198C** | | WRC | 65 | 79 | Derbyshire Fire Service | B3 Darleston Rd-Glossop-**Converted Tanker**<br>Laird-Butterfield |
| **JLL878D** | **1145** | FOT | 66 | 83 | Merseyside Fire Brigade | **ex Tanker-Converted 1977**<br>W1 Exmouth St-Birkenhead-1983<br>Comet- |
| **JLL898D** | | WRC | 67 | 82 | Derbyshire Fire Service | **ex Tanker-Converted 1976**/A02 Tamworth Rd-Long Eaton<br>Laird-Butterfield |
| **618UZ** | | WRC | 67 | 83 | Derbyshire Fire Service | **ex Tanker-Converted 1978**/C1 Sheffield Rd-Chesterfield<br>Laird-DFB |
| **STX321F** | | Rec/V | 68 | ? | Glamorgan Fire Service (Wales) | B1 Sunnyside-Bridgend- |
| **SMD657F** | | Foam Tanker | 68 | 93 | Essex County Fire Brigade | C68 Laindon Rd-Billericay/D87 Stortford Rd-Gt Dunmow<br>Super Comet-ECFB |
| **ANY168H** | | Rec/V | 70 | ? | Glamorgan Fire Service (Wales) | Brigade Workshops |
| **CCH132H** | | WRC | 70 | 84 | Staffordshire Fire Brigade | Rugeley Fire Station-1974/Bryans Lane-Rugeley-1984<br>Comet-Butterfield |
| **FCH261J** | | WRC | 71 | 84 | Staffordshire Fire Brigade | Old Hednesford Rd-Cannock<br>Boxer-Swan |
| **YAF725J** | | WRC | 71 | 87 | Cornwall County Fire Brigade | B1 Berrycombe Rd-Bodmin<br>Laird-Fergusson |
| **WKR152J** | | WRC | 71 | ? | Kent Fire Brigade | 65 New Hythe Rd-Larkfield<br>Laird- |

| | | | | | | |
|---|---|---|---|---|---|---|
| EYE914J | | FOT | 71 | 83 | Merseyside Fire Brigade | ex Tanker-Converted 1978-N1 Strand Rd-Bootle-1979<br>N1 Buckley Hill Lane-Netherton-1983   Laird-MFB |
| GOT356K | | WRC<br>FOC | 72 | | Hampshire Fire Service | B17 Station Approach-Fareham<br>Mastiff-Fergusson |
| GOT357K | | WRC<br>FOC | 72 | | Hampshire Fire Service | A01 West Ham Close-Basingstoke<br>Mastiff-Fergusson |
| GAF94L | | WRC | 72 | 88 | Cornwall County Fire Brigade | A4 College St-Camborne<br>Boxer-Fergusson |
| JCV716L | | WRC | 73 | 89 | Cornwall County Fire Brigade | A1 Station Rd-Truro<br>Boxer-Fergusson |
| KIA6917 | | FOT | 76 | | Northern Ireland Fire Brigade | D02 Crescent Link-Londonderry<br>Lynx-Carmichael |
| KTR891P | | WRC | 76 | | Hampshire Fire Service | D58 Falconer Court-Fawley<br>Mastiff-Fergusson |
| RYA679R | | WRC | 77 | 87 | Dorset Fire Brigade | B15 Worget Rd-Wareham<br>Tanker chassied onto Volvo FL6 -K907VRU<br>Clydesdale-Wincanton |
| PPX512S | | WRC<br>FOC | 78 | | Hampshire Fire Service | C31 London Rd-Andover<br>Mastiff-Fergusson |
| UCY71S | | PM<br>FOT | 78 | 92 | West Glamorgan County Fire Service<br>(Wales) | 1 Cimla Rd-Neath<br>Mastiff-Powell Duffryn |
| UCY72S | | PM<br>FOT | 78 | 92 | West Glamorgan County Fire Service<br>(Wales) | 5 Grove Place-Swansea<br>8 Sway Rd-Morriston-Swansea-1982<br>Mastiff-Powell Duffryn |
| PIA5790 | | FOT | 80 | | Northern Ireland Fire Brigade | A08 Whitla St-Whitla-Belfast<br>Lynx-Carmichael |
| JPH84V | | WRC | 80 | | Wiltshire Fire Brigade | ex Milk Tanker -1/6 Station Rd-Wooton Bassett<br>Clydesdale-Wincanton |
| XYA369W | | WRC | 80 | | Wiltshire Fire Brigade | ex Milk Tanker -3/2 Minster St-Wilton<br>Clydesdale-Wincanton |
| WYC983W | | WRC | 80 | | Wiltshire Fire Brigade | ex Milk Tanker -4/5 The Portway-Warminster<br>Clydesdale-Wincanton |

**BDY509 was built in 1939 by Leyland Motors. This FK Cub Limousine model was used as a Pump Emergency Tender for the County Borough of Hastings and was based at Bohemia Road in Hastings for almost 30 years. The picture shows that there was little room for the officer to gain access when in full dress.**
*Keith Wardell collection*

**Leyland DAF 17-18  G505XFH** was an emergency support unit delivered to Gloucester complete with a white cab. It features a rear mounted Hiab 071 crane that brought an additional dimension to its rescue capabilities.  This machine marked a return of 'Leyland DAF' to the Heavy Rescue/Emergency Tender market and also saw a return to the old Gloucestershire tradition of operating a Heavy Recovery unit. *Clive Shearman*

Cornwall County ordered three water carriers on to be based on Leyland chassis. The first carried badges for the Laird chassis while the latter examples arrived as the Boxer following the re-naming of the model. GAF94L, shown here, was allocated to Camborne when photographed. Since withdrawal, one of the batch has found its way to Africa for use there appliances where they displace even older appliances.
*Michael Lawmon*

| | | | | | | |
|---|---|---|---|---|---|---|
| GFS75X | | HLL | 82 | | Fife Fire Brigade (Scotland) | Thornton Headquarters Terrier-FFB |
| BPG774Y | | Rec/V | 82 | | Surrey Fire & Rescue Service | Brigade Workshops T50-Wreckers International |
| SKG271Y | | PM CIU | 83 | | South Glamorgan County FS-**1996** South Wales Fire Service (Wales) | 3 Heol y Nant-Whitchurch Terrier-Powell Duffryn-Rolonoff |
| A512EPB | | WRC | 84 | | Wiltshire Fire Brigade | **ex Milk Tanker-**1/3 High St-Ramsbury Clydesdale-Wincanton |
| B243NPF | S00006 | WRC | 85 | | Suffolk Fire Service | 01 Colchester Rd-Ipswich Daf 16-17-Dairy Crest |
| C837YVF | | C/Unit | 85 | | Norfolk Fire Brigade | 31 London Rd-Wymondham Freight Rover Sherpa 350-NFB |
| C738HYC | | FSU | 86 | | Somerset Fire Brigade | A01 Lisieux Way-Taunton Freight Rover Sherpa 300-SFB |
| C739HYC | | FSU | 86 | | Somerset Fire Brigade | B21 Reckleford-Yeovil Freight Rover Sherpa 300-SFB |
| C538YRJ | | Hi ex Foam Unit | 86 | | Greater Manchester County Fire Service | B23 Albert Rd-Farnworth Roadrunner-GMCFS |
| C532YRU | | BAT | 86 | 94 | Dorset Fire Brigade | A07 North Quay-Weymouth Roadrunner-Spectre |
| D576OOM | BAT2 | BAT | 86 | | Warwickshire Fire & Rescue Service | **ex 29 Royal Leamington Spa-1992** 24 Kings Ave-Atherstone Freight Rover Sherpa 300-WF&RS |

| | | | | | |
|---|---|---|---|---|---|
| D90OVM | | Rec/V | 87 | Greater Manchester County Fire Service | Brigade Workshops<br>T180-Wreckers International |
| D624DTR | | WRC<br>FOC | 87 | Hampshire Fire Service | C29 Steele Close-Eastleigh<br>Daf 16-17-Buckingham Tankers |
| E823SOJ | 308 | PM /FDU<br>ISU | 88 | West Midlands Fire Service | A5 College Rd-Perry Bar<br>Freighter 16-17-Multilift-Keyway |
| F726RAB | | PM<br>BAT | 88 | Hereford & Worcester Fire Brigade | Training Centre-Droitwich<br>Freighter 14-16-Multilift-Penman |
| G999PTV | CV-02 | CAV | 90 | Derbyshire Fire Service | C02 Market St-Clay Cross<br>Roadrunner-Frank Guy-DFS |
| G998RFM | | C/Unit<br>CAV | 90 | Cheshire Fire Brigade | A5 Sadler Rd-Winsford / **Articulated Unit**<br>Roadrunner-Gordons |
| G999RFM | | C/Unit<br>CAV | 90 | Cheshire Fire Brigade | A4 Braden Close-Northwich/ **Articulated Unit**<br>Roadrunner-Gordons |
| G580YJU | | C/Unit | 90 | Leicestershire Fire & Rescue Service | Brigade Headquarters-1995/SD Leicester South<br>Dart-LF&RS |
| G500JFR | 30428 | C/Unit<br>CAV | 90 | Lancashire County Fire Brigade | C52 Garstang Rd-Fulwood<br>Swift-Reeves Burgess |
| H311CDL | | BAT | 91 | Isle of Wight Fire & Rescue Service | 01 South St-Newport<br>Daf Sherpa 400-IoWF&RS |
| J671BUY | | WRC<br>FOC | 91 | Hereford & Worcester Fire Brigade | ND 24 Castle Rd-Kidderminster<br>Daf 20-210-Dairy Crest |
| J781HCA | | SIU | 92 | Cheshire Fire Brigade | A2 Wellington Rd-Ellesmere Port<br>10-15-Linton |
| J299HCA | | SIU | 92 | Cheshire Fire Brigade | C1 Macon Way-Crewe<br>10-15-Linton |
| K241VJO | | Salv/T | 93 | Buckinghamshire Fire & Rescue Service | High St-Great Missenden<br>Daf Sherpa 400-Reliance Mercury |
| K128XRJ | | BAT | 93 | Greater Manchester County Fire Service | B21 Compton Way-Bolton<br>Daf Freighter T45-Bedwas |
| K129XRJ | | BAT | 93 | Greater Manchester County Fire Service | E57 Railway St-Hyde<br>Daf Freighter T45-Bedwas |
| L728BFX | | BAT | 93 | Dorset Fire Brigade | B26 Fairmile Rd-Christchurch<br>Daf Freighter T45-Locomotors |
| L729BFX | | BAT | 93 | Dorset Fire Brigade | A07 North Quay-Weymouth<br>Daf-Freighter T45-Locomotors |
| M701UHG | 30048 | PMover<br>FOT/DC<br>U BAT | 95 | Lancashire County Fire Brigade | 90 Belvedere Rd-Burnley<br>Daf 60-Multilift-Bedwas |
| M702UHG | 30049 | PMover<br>FoT/CIU | 95 | Lancashire County Fire Brigade | 50 Blackpool Rd-Preston<br>Daf 60-Multilift-Bedwas |
| M703UHG | 30050 | PMover<br>MIS/Unit | 95 | Lancashire County Fire Brigade | 50 Blackpool Rd-Preston<br>Daf 60-Multilift-Bedwas |
| N814MFH | 773 | Foam<br>Support/U | 95 | Gloucestershire Fire & Rescue Service | 07 Pagen Hill Rd-Stroud<br>Daf FA45-W H Bence |
| N815MFH | 774 | Water/C<br>Foam/U | 95 | Gloucestershire Fire & Rescue Service | 12 Keynsham Rd-Cheltenham<br>Daf T60-210/Massey Tankers |
| N818MFH | 776 | HGV<br>GPV | 95 | Gloucestershire Fire & Rescue Service | Training Centre<br>Daf FA45-WH Bence |
| P371VDG | 787 | PMover | 96 | Gloucestershire Fire & Rescue Service | Training Centre<br>Daf FA45-WH Bence |

# MERRYWEATHER

| Reg No | Fleet No | TYPE | YR | OS | BRIGADE | Details/Stations |
|---|---|---|---|---|---|---|
| | NFS Merryweather Ladder No MW | | | | | The Merryweather Ladder was supplied on its own chassis with either a Dorman 6 cylinder engine or a Meadows 6 cylinder engine. |
| ? | | TL | 20 | **42 ?** | Surrey County Council FB | Farnham Fire Station<br>Merryweather-85 L Wooden-**Dorman** |
| CL 416 | | TL | 21 | 37 | City of Norwich | Pottergate Fire Station-Norwich<br>Merryweather-85 L Wooden-**Dorman** |
| ? | | TL | 21 | ? | City of Portsmouth | ?<br>Merryweather-85 L Wooden-**Dorman** |
| UM6396 | MW-1 | TLP | 28 | 47 | Leeds City Fire Brigade | Various Leeds Fire Stations-**Hatfield Pump & Moniter**<br>Merryweather-85'L-Wooden-**250gpmP-Dorman** |
| ? | | TL | 28 | ? | Luton County Borough Fire Brigade | ?<br>Merryweather 85 L Wooden-**Dorman** |
| ? | | TL | 28 | **45 ?** | Burton upon Trent Fire Brigade | ?<br>Merryweather 85 L Wooden-**Dorman** |
| XG 488 | MW-4 | TL | 30 | 48 | Middlesbrough Fire Brigade | **Ladder housed at North Ormesby Road Bus Garage-1939 Crew went by taxi to man it when required.**<br>Park Road South-Middlesbrough-1948<br>Merryweather-85 L Wooden-**500gpmP-Dorman** |
| HY 113 | MW-5 | TL | 30 | 46 | City of Bristol | #1 Bridewell St-Bristol<br>**Converted to 100 Steel in 1941**<br>Merryweather-85 L Wooden-**Dorman** |
| EF4475 | MW-6 | TLP | 31 | 48 | West Hartlepool Fire Brigade | Barnard St-West Hartlepool<br>Merryweather-85 L Wooden-**275gpmP-Dorman** |
| JK2392 | MW-7 | TL | 33 | 46 | Eastbourne County Borough FB | Grove Rd-Eastbourne-1942 / Bourne St-Eastbourne-1946<br>Merryweather-85'L Wooden-**Dorman** |
| JY937 | MW-8 | TL | 32 | 46 | City of Plymouth | Greenbank Rd-Plymouth-Devon<br>Merryweather-85'-Wooden-**Dorman** |
| APU459 | MW-9 | TLP | 33 | 59 | Ilford Fire Brigade | Ley St-Ilford-1947 / Leytonstone- Essex-1959<br>Merryweather-85'L-Steel-**400gpmP-Dorman** |
| AVR1 | MW-10 | TL | 34 | 50 | City of Manchester | London Rd-Manchester-1942 / Wilmslow Rd-Withington-1950      Merryweather-100'L-**Dorman** |
| AER2 | MW-11 | TLP | 34 | 54 | Cambridgeshire Fire Brigade | St Andrews-Cambridge<br>Merryweather-85'L-**400gpmP-Dorman** |
| AFJ282 | MW-12 | TLP | 34 | 57 | City of Exeter | Danes Castle-Exeter-1946<br>Stockton-Durham County FB-1948<br>Merryweather-85'L-**400gpmP-Dorman** |
| WS3074 | MW-14 | TLP | 35 | 48 | City of Edingburgh (Scotland) | Leith Fire Station-Edingburgh<br>Merryweather-105'L |
| CMF366 | TLP5<br>MW-15 | TLP | 35 | 57 | Hornsey Fire Brigade | Tottenham Lane-Hornsey-Middlesex 1948<br>Chapel Lane-Wigan CBFB-1957<br>Merryweather-85'L-**350gpmP-Dorman** |
| JV3950 | MW-16 | TLP | 35 | 43 | Grimsby Fire Brigade | Alexandra Rd-Grimsby<br>Merryweather-100'L-**400gpmP-Dorman** |
| JF9386 | MW-17 | TLP | 35 | ? | City of Leicester | Lancaster Place-Leicester<br>Merryweather-100'L-**400gpmP-Dorman** |
| CAE965 | MW-18 | TLP | 36 | 48 | Bristol Police Fire Brigade | #1 Bridewell St-Bristol-1948<br>Merryweather-100'L-**300gpmP-Dorman** |
| EML219 | TLP3<br>MW-19 | TLP | 36 | 54 | Acton Fire Brigade | Gunnersbury Lane-Acton-Middlesex<br>Merryweather-100'L-**550gpmP-Meadows** |

| DKL730 | MW-20 | TLP | 36 | 57 | Kent Fire Brigade | A Div-South St-Bromley<br>Merryweather-85'L-**4/600gpmP-Meadows** |
|---|---|---|---|---|---|---|
| GL4110 | MW-21 | TLP | 37 | 58 | City of Bath | #1 Cleveland Bridge-Bath<br>**Ladders Re-chassied onto AEC Regent-GFB712**<br>Merryweather-85'L-400gpmP-Meadows |
| VG9792 | MW-22 | TLP | 37 | 62 | City of Norwich | Bethel St-Norwich-1962<br>Merryweather-100'L-**500gpmP-Meadows** |
| HV8139 | MW-23 | TLP | 37 | ? | East Ham County Borough | High St-East Ham<br>Merryweather-75'L-**600gpm-Meadows** |
| GMC983 | TLP2<br>MW-24 | TLP | 37 | 60 | Edmonton Fire Brigade | Church St-Edmonton-Middlesex-1948<br>Watford-Hertfordshire-1960<br>Merrweather-85'L-**450gpmP-Meadows** |
| EKP395 | MW-26 | TLP | 38 | 58 | Kent Fire Brigade | D Div-Park Farm Rd-Folkestone<br>**Ladders Re-chassied onto AEC Regent-YKP177**<br>Merryweather-100 L-**500gpmP-Meadows** |
| FHT674 | MW-29 | TLP | 38 | 68 | Bristol Police Fire Brigade | #1 Bridewell St-1940/ # 3 Avonmouth-Bristol-1958<br>Reserve-1968/City of Bristol FB-**Preserved**<br>Merryweather-**100'L-300gpmP-Meadows** |
| FEL623 | MW-30 | TLP | 38 | 58 | Bournemouth County Borough FB | Holdenhurst Rd-Bournemouth<br>Merryweather-100'L-**450gpmP-Meadows** |
| HVW107 | MW-31 | TLP | 39 | 56 | Essex County Fire Brigade | Burnham Rd South-Dagenham-1954/Reserve-1956<br>Merryweather-100'L-**500gpmP-Meadows** |
| JEV802 | MW-32 | TLP | 38 | 71 | Barking Fire Brigade | Alfreds Way-Barking-Essex<br>**Sold to Westgate Brewery-1971 /Preserved**<br>Merryweather-100'L-**500gpmP-Meadows** |

Delivered new to the Acton Fire Brigade at the old Gunnersbury Lane station, EML219 passed, in 1947, to the then newly formed Middlesex Fire Brigade. This vehicle had a Meadows 6-cylinder engine that also powered a 550 gpm pump.
Visible are the Firefighters period boots, ready for donning in anticipation of the next shout.
*Roy Goodey*

# 4x4 & 6x4 WHEEL DRIVE

| Reg No | Fleet No | TYPE | YR | OS | Appliance & Brigade Name | Details/Stations |
|---|---|---|---|---|---|---|
| | | | | | **Land Rover**<br>**Chassied Appliances** | **The list does not include details on the hundreds of Land Rovers which have been used as Light Four Wheel Drive Pumping Appliances.** |
| **Type**<br>**Series 1**<br>**Series 2**<br>**Series 2A**<br>**FT Series**<br>**Forward- Control** | | | 50s<br>60s<br>60s<br>60s<br>70s | | **Wheelbase**<br>**88ins**<br>**109ins**<br>**110ins**<br>**110ins** | **The Rover Company produced its first Land Rover in 1949. Its chassis weight was 1500cwt with a wheelbase of 7ft 4ins. It was powered by a 1600cc engine. The wheelbase was extended in later models as in the 109 Normal Control and 110 in the later FT Series and Forward Control models which had a heavier payload. When water tanks were carried they had a capacity of approx 100gallons and first aid hose reels powered by a Coventry Climax pump.** |
| **PHY205** | | Res/T | 52 | 65 | City of Bristol | 3 St Andrews Rd-Avonmouth<br>88 NC-CoBFB |
| **LYO837** | | CRU | 53 | 73 | Eastbourne County Borough Fire Brigade | **ex Auxillary Fire Service** /Bourne St-Eastbourne<br>Whitley Rd-Eastbourne-1973<br>88 NC- |
| **FF8721** | **10** | LRP | 53 | ? | Merionethshire County Borough (Wales) | Harlech Fire Station-1975<br>24 Harlech -Gwynedd Fire Service<br>88 NC-Carmichael |
| **FF9728** | **11** | LRP | 55 | ? | Merionethshire County Borough (Wales) | Blaenau Ffestiniog-1975<br>26 Blaenau Ffestiniog-1979-Gwynedd Fire Service<br>88 NC-Carmichael |
| **WLG671** | **1006** | L4P | 55 | 79 | Cheshire Fire Brigade | D8 Dock Rd South-Bebbington-1962<br>**Converted to Hi ex FOT**<br>D8 Dock Rd South-Bebbington-1974<br>W2 Dock Rd South-Bebbington-1979/Merseyside Fire Brigade            88 NC-CFB |
| **6BMA** | | L4P | 56 | ? | Cheshire Fire Brigade | C3/A4 Braden Close-Northwich-1965<br>**Converted Hi ex FOT**/C3/A4-Northwich-1974-**L4V**<br>88 NC-CCFB |
| **YTU390** | | L4P | 57 | ? | Cheshire Fire Brigade | A5 Hollins Lane-Marple-1962<br>**Converted Hi ex FOT**-A2 Ramsbottom St-Stalybridge-1974<br>E55 Ramsbottom Rd-Stalybridge-1975<br>Greater Manchester CFS<br>88 NC-CCFB |
| **SXF739** | | ET | 57 | 75 | City of Chester | **ex Auxillary Fire Service**-A1 St Anne's St-Chester-1974<br>A1 St Annes St-Chester-1975 -Cheshire Fire Brigade<br>109- |
| **478CMB** | | L4P | 58 | 78 | Cheshire Fire Brigade | B1/C5 Altrincham Rd-Wilmslow-1972<br>**Converted to Hi ex FOT**<br>B1/C5 Altrincham Rd-Wilmslow-1978-**L4V**<br>109- |
| **2273AC** | | ET | 58 | 80 | Warwick County Fire Brigade | 51 Masons Ave- Stratford on Avon 1962<br>**Converted Lighting unit**<br>41 Warwick St-Royal Leamington Spa -1976<br>42 Albert St-Warwick-1980<br>109-Carmichael |
| **WCG313** | | Res/T | 59 | 79 | Hampshire Fire Brigade | C30 North Walls-Winchester<br>109-HFB |
| **YOR203** | | Res/T | 59 | 84 | Hampshire Fire Brigade | A2 Grovesnor Rd-Aldershot-1972<br>A2 Ordenance Rd-Aldershot-1976<br>A5 Butts Rd-Alton-1984            109-HFS |

| | | | | | | |
|---|---|---|---|---|---|---|
| **JGS652** | | ET | 59 | ? | Perth & Kinross Fire Brigade (Scotland) | High St-Perth 109-P&KFB |
| **WDF99** | | Light Unit | 60 | 75 | Gloucestershire Fire Service | 07 Pagenhill Lane-Stroud 109-GFS |
| **465ERT** | | RAV | 60 | 79 | Suffolk & Ipswich Fire Service | 109-S&IFS |
| **466ERT** | | RAV | 60 | 79 | Suffolk & Ipswich Fire Service | 109-S&IFS |
| **250HRT** | | RAV | 61 | 79 | Suffolk & Ipswich Fire Service | 109-S&IFS |
| **SGS535** | | ERT | 61 | 78 | Perth & Kinross Fire Brigade (Scotland) | Atholl Rd-Pitlochry-1975 B7 Atholl Rd-Pitlochry-1978-Tayside Fire Brigade 109-P&KFB |
| **SMS682** | | L4V Res/T | 61 | 82 | Central Area Fire Brigade (Scotland) | Ranoch Rd-Stirling-1975 S8 Ranoch Rd-Stirling-1982-Central Region Fire Brigade 108-Fire Armour |
| **SMS684** | | L4V Res/T | 61 | 81 | Central Area Fire Brigade (Scotland) | Castlegreen St-Dumbarton-1975. F7 Castlegreen Rd-Dumbarton-**Converted Road Rescue Unit**          Strathclyde Fire Brigade 108-Fire Armour |
| **PGS442** | | ET | 61 | ? | Perth & Kinross Fire Brigade (Scotland) | High St-Perth-1968-Anderson St-Dunblane-1975 S6 Anderson St-Dunblane -**Converted to L4V**-Crianlarich Central Region Fire Brigade 108-P&KFB |
| **422RMB** | | L4P | 61 | 78 | Cheshire Fire Brigade | D6/A2 Wellington Rd-1974-**Converted to Hi ex FOT** C3/A4 Braddon Close-Northwich-1978-**L4V** 109- |

Land Rover 109 MFB471 was a dual purpose Rescue Tender and Lighting Unit that serving at the Cleveland Bridge station in Bath. It was delivered in 1961 fitted with Carmichael bodywork and served for more than twenty years. The photograph shows the very large roof-mounted searchlight which it retains in its current preserved state.
*Keith Wardell collection*

| | | | | | | |
|---|---|---|---|---|---|---|
| MFB471 | | RAV | 61 | 73 | City of Bath | Cleveland Bridge-Bath-1974<br>B1 Cleveland Bridge-Bath-1975-**Lighting Unit-1975**<br>109-Carmichael |
| MGL423 | | Foam/C | 61 | 75 | City of Bath | Cleveland Bridge-Bath-1974<br>B1 Cleveland Bridge-Bath-1975-County of Avon FB<br>109-CoBFB |
| FFF169 | 17 | L4R | 61 | 88 | Merionethshire County Borough (Wales) | Park Rd-Barmouth-1975/20 Park Rd-Barmouth-1977<br>23 Cardiff Rd-Pwllhelli-1988-Gwynedd Fire Service<br>110-Forward Control-Carmichael |
| 4108KC | | Res/T | 62 | 74 | City of Liverpool | #6 Banks Rd-Liverpool-1965/Liverpool (Speke) Airport-1975    109- |
| 530CBD | | Res/T | 62 | 81 | Northamptonshire Fire Brigade | N01 The Headlands-Kettering-1972<br>A10 Irthlingborough Rd-Wellingborough-1981<br>109-NFB |
| 290GAC | | L4P | 62 | 77 | Warwick County Fire Brigade | 21 Newtown Rd-Nuneaton<br>**Converted to Emergency Tender**<br>21 Newtown Rd-Nuneaton-1974/Reserve-1977<br>110-Forward Control-Carmichael |
| 291GAC | | L4P | 62 | 78 | Warwick County Fire Brigade | 51 Masons Ave-Stratford on Avon **Converted to ET**<br>51 Masons Ave-Stratford on Avon<br>110-Forward Control-Carmichael |
| WBF7 | | Res/T | 62 | 73 | Staffordshire Fire Brigade | Stafford Fire Station-1965/Wombourne Fire Station-1971<br>Giggetty Lane-Wombourne-1973<br>109-Mumfords |
| VDJ319 | 1048 | HLL | 63 | 82 | St Helens County Borough Fire Brigade | #1 Parr Stocks Rd-St Helens-1970<br>#2 Millfields Rd-Eccleston-1974<br>E5 Millfields Rd-Eccleston-1982-Merseyside Fire Brigade<br>**Liverpool (Speke) Airport Res/T**<br>110-Forward Control-F&D |
| 87HOR | | Res/T | 63 | 81 | Hampshire Fire Brigade | B17 West St-Fareham-1972<br>B17 Station Approach-Fareham-1974<br>B16 Parkway-Havant-1981<br>109-HFS |
| 88HOR | | Res/T | 63 | 79 | Hampshire Fire Brigade | D48 High St-Lyndhurst-1976<br>D48 Southampton Rd-Lyndhurst-1979<br>109-HFS |
| 15BMR | | Res/T | 63 | 81 | Wiltshire Fire Brigade | **ex L4P** - 2/1 Chipenham Fire Station-1974<br>2/1 Dallas Rd-Chippenham-1976-**L4V-1/3 Ramsbury-1981**<br>109-WFB |
| 16BMR | | FOT | 63 | 82 | Wiltshire Fire Brigade | **ex L4V** - 4/3 Melksham Fire Station-1968<br>4/3 Semington Rd-Melksham-**L4V-3/7 Pewsey-1982**<br>109-WFB |
| CCC149<br>KSU927 | | L4R | 64 | 91 | Caernarvonshire County Council (Wales) | Dolydd Rd-Betws y Coed-1974<br>05 Bangor Rd-Conwy-1991-Gwynedd Fire Service<br>110-Forward Control-Carmichael |
| ERF723B | | Res/T | 64 | ? | Staffordshire Fire Brigade | Birmingham Rd-Lichfield -**Snow Plough-date**<br>109-Mumford |
| ERF724B | | Res/T | 64 | 73 | Staffordshire Fire Brigade | Newcastle Fire Station-1965/Knutton Lane-Lichfield-1973<br>109-Mumford |
| BHR459B | | Decon Unit | 64 | 86 | Wiltshire Fire Brigade | **ex Hose Reel Tender-1/1 Swindon**-1/1 Drove Rd-Swindon<br>**L4V-1/3 Ramsbury-1986**<br>109-Carmichael |
| BHR460B | | Decon Unit | 64 | 86 | Wiltshire Fire Brigade | **ex Hose Reel Tender-3/1 Sailsbury**<br>3/1 Ashley Rd-Sailsbury-**L4V-3/1 Sailsbury-1986**<br>109-Carmichael |
| CNT322B | | Res/T | 64 | 78 | Shropshire Fire Service | St Michael's St-Shrewsbury<br>FT6-Carmichael |

| | | | | | | |
|---|---|---|---|---|---|---|
| **BFS330B** | | ET | 64 | 78 | South Eastern Area Fire Brigade (Scotland) | Glasgow Rd-Bathgate-1975<br>54 Glasgow Rd-Bathgate-1978-Lothian & Borders FB<br>110 Forward Control-Merryweather |
| **BUD892B** | | HLL | 64 | 76 | Oxfordshire Fire Service | A06 Sterling Rd Kidlington<br>110 Forward Control-Jones |
| **EFS999C** | | ET | 65 | 80 | South Eastern Area Fire Brigade (Scotland) | Abbotsford Rd-Galashiels-1975<br>34 Abbotsford Rd-Galashiels-1980-Lothian & Borders FB<br>110 Forward Control-Merryweather |
| **DHN999C** | | ET | 65 | 88 | Darlington County Borough Fire Brigade | Borough Rd-Darlington-1972<br>St Cuthberts Way-Darlington-1974<br>S1 St Cuthberts Way-Darlington-1988-Durham County FB<br>109- |
| **YRE638C** | | Res/T | 65 | 78 | Staffordshire Fire Brigade | Leek Fire Station-1971 /Springfield Rd-Leek-1978<br>109-Carmichael |
| **FPM661C** | | Res/T | 65 | ? | East Sussex Fire Brigade | 18 High St-Battle-1973<br>109-Carmichael |
| **EHR124C** | | FOT BAT | 65 | 84 | Wiltshire Fire Brigade | **ex L4V** - 4/1 Hilperton Rd-Trowbridge-1980-**L4V-4/6 Devizes-1984**          109-WFB |
| **EHR125C** | | Res/T | 65 | 87 | Wiltshire Fire Brigade | 1/5 The Parade-Marlborough-1976-**L4V-1/4 Stratton-1990**<br>109-WFB |
| **LTG349D** | | L4P | 66 | ? | Glamorgan County Fire Brigade (Wales) | B6 Barry Fire Station-1974<br>2 Colchester Ave-Roath-Cardiff-1985<br>**Converted to Hose Layer**<br>4 Cowbridge Rd West-Ely-Cardiff-1986-South Glamorgan<br>109-GFB |
| **HNT936D** | | Res/T | 66 | 78 | Shropshire Fire Service | Haybridge Rd-Wellington<br>FT6-Carmichael |
| **FMW701D** | | Res/T | 66 | 90 | Wiltshire Fire Brigade | **ex L4V**- 3/4 Mere Fire Station-1972<br>3/4 White Rd-Mere-1978-**L4V-3/4 Mere-1990**<br>109-WFB |
| **FMW702D** | | FOT HLL | 66 | 85 | Wiltshire Fire Brigade | **ex L4V** - 1/1 Drove Rd-Swindon -**L4V-2/4 Calne-1985**<br>109-WFB |
| **FMW703D** | | Res/T | 66 | 92 | Wiltshire Fire Brigade | **ex HRT**- 2/3 Malmesbury Fire Station-1969<br>2/3 Gloucester Rd-Malmesbury-1979<br>**L4V-2/3 Malmesbury-1992**<br>109-WFB |
| **GRR999D** | | Res/T | 66 | 79 | Nottinghamshire Fire Brigade | 16 Boundary Rd-Newark<br>109-Mann Egerton |
| **GNN999D** | | Res/T | 66 | 76 | Nottinghamshire Fire Brigade | 12 Wharf Rd-Retford<br>109-Mann Egerton |
| **GVO999D** | | Res/T | 66 | 78 | Nottinghamshire Fire Brigade | 05 Kirkby Rd-Sutton in Ashfield<br>109-Mann Egerton |
| **GAA216D** | | Res/T | 67 | 76 | Hampshire Fire Brigade | A1 West Ham Close-Basingstoke-1970 Reserve-1976<br>109-HFB |
| **LNN999E** | | Res/T | 67 | ? | Nottinghamshire Fire Brigade | 22 Station Rd-Beeston<br>109-Mann Egerton |
| **JHR485E** | | Res/T | 67 | 86 | Wiltshire Fire Brigade | 4/6 Devizes Fire Station-1969<br>4/6 Southbroom Rd-Devizes-1977<br>**L4V-2/1 Chippenham-1986**<br>109-WFB |
| **JHR486E** | | Res/T | 67 | | Wiltshire Fire Brigade | 3/6 Castle St-Ludgershall-1978<br>**L4V-4/1 Trowbridge-1985-L4V-4/5 Warminster-**<br>109-WFB |
| **GCE481E** | | Res/T | 67 | 82 | Cambridgeshire Fire & Rescue Service | N20 Horsefair-Wisbech<br>110-Forward Control-CF&RS |
| **KWF286E** | | Res/T | 67 | 82 | East Riding of Yorkshire Fire Brigade | #2 Bessingby Rd-Bridlington-1974<br>B3 Bessingby Rd-Bridlington-1976<br>A4 Albert Terrace-Beverley-1984/Humberside Fire Brigade<br>109-Carmichael |

| | | | | | | |
|---|---|---|---|---|---|---|
| KWF287E | | Res/T | 67 | 84 | East Riding of Yorkshire Fire Brigade | #1 Albert Terrace-Beverley-1974<br>A4 Albert Terrace-Beverley-1976<br>C1 Peakes Lane-Grimsby-1984 /Humberside Fire Brigade<br>109-Carmichael |
| KAD702E | | Hi-ex FOT | 67 | 79 | Gloucestershire Fire Service | 07 Pagenhill Lane-Stroud<br>109-GFS |
| MCG558F | | Res/T | 67 | 81 | Hampshire Fire Brigade | C31 London Rd-Andover-        /-L4V<br>109-HFB |
| JWL940F | 10 | Hi ex FOT | 68 | 76 | City of Oxford | ex L4P / Rewley Rd-Oxford-1974<br>B01 Rewley Rd-Oxford-1976-Oxfordshire Fire Service<br>110-Carmichael |
| NHY999F | | Res/T | 68 | 76 | City of Bristol | 3 St Andrews Rd-Avonmouth-1974<br>A3 St Andrews Rd-Avonmouth-1976-County of Avon FB<br>109-Carmichael |
| VRB494F | | Res/T | 68 | 76 | Derbyshire Fire Service | B4 Chesterfield Rd-Matlock<br>110-Forward Control-Merryweather |
| VRB495F | | Res/T | 68 | 86 | Derbyshire Fire Service | B1 Campton Grove-Buxton-1981<br>Converted Breathing AppT<br>B1 Campton Grove-Buxton-1986<br>110-FC-Merryweather-Re-bodied-Reeve Burgess |
| SRM165G | | Res/T | 68 | ? | Cumberland County Fire Brigade | N21 Bridge Lane-Penrith-1974 /Bridge Lane-Penrith-1984<br>Converted Light Pump<br>Mill Lane-Walney-Cumbria Fire Service<br>109-        / Re-bodied Carmichael |
| YRB961G | | Res/T | 68 | 75 | Derbyshire Fire Service | A3 Derby Rd-Ripley<br>110-Forward Control-Merryweather |
| YRB962G | | Res/T | 68 | | Derbyshire Fire Service | A2 Tamworth Rd-Long Eaton<br>110-Forward Control-Merryweather |
| OOU491G | | Res/T | 68 | 77 | Hampshire Fire Brigade | A14 Swan St-Petersfield-1977-L4V<br>110-Forward Control-HCB Angus |
| YWE496G | | Res/T | 69 | | City of Sheffield | #2 Darnall Rd-Sheffield<br>110-Forward Control-Merryweather |
| XPF335G | | Accident Res/V | 69 | 79 | Surrey County Council Fire Brigade | London Rd-Camberley-1973-Reserve-1979<br>108-SCCFB |
| WFD578H | | Res/T | 69 | | Dudley County Borough Fire Brigade | Tower Rd-Dudley<br>108- |
| NBX305H | | ET | 70 | 81 | Carmarthen & Cardiganshire (Wales) | Trefechan-Aberyswyth-1974<br>C1 Trefechan-Aberyswyth-1981-Dyfed Fire Brigade<br>109-Carmichael |
| NBX306H | | ET | 70 | 80 | Carmarthen & Cardiganshire (Wales) | Corporation Ave-Llanelli-1974<br>A1 Corporation Ave-Llanelli-1980-Dyfed Fire Brigade<br>109-Carmichael |
| NBX881H | | ET | 70 | 81 | Carmarthen & Cardiganshire (Wales) | Lime Grove Ave-Carmarthen-1974<br>B1 Lime Grove Ave-Carmarthen-1980-Dyfed Fire Brigade<br>109-Carmichael |
| URM486H | | Res/T | 70 | ? | Cumberland County Fire Brigade | W10 King St-Workington-1974 /CD King St-Workington-1977   Converted to Light Pump<br>AD Warwick St-Carlisle-Cumbria Fire Service<br>109-        /Re-bodied Carmichael |
| UNW805H | | RAV | 70 | 78 | Leeds City Fire Brigade | Kirkstall Rd-Leeds-1974<br>Training School-1978-West Yorkshire Fire Service<br>110-Forward Control-Stokell |
| DWE948H | | Res/T | 70 | ? | City of Sheffield | #5 Elm Lane-Sheffield-        South Yorkshire County FS<br>109-Merryweather |
| XTG925H | 22 | Res/T HLL | 70 | 86 | Glamorgan County Fire Brigade (Wales) | 3 Heol y Nant-Whitchurch-1977<br>5 Port Rd-West-Barry-1984<br>B7 Llanmaes Rd-Llantwit Major-1974<br>8 Llanmaes Rd-Llantwit Major-1986-South Glamorgan CFS<br>109-Hoskins-GFB |

| | | | | | | |
|---|---|---|---|---|---|---|
| TWO864H | | Res/T | 70 | | Monmouthshire Fire Brigade (Wales) | Abercarn Fire Station-1974/C5 Darren Drive-Abercarn-1976 **Converted to L4P-C06 Tredegar-**Gwent Fire Brigade 109-MFB |
| TWO865H | | Res/T | 70 | | Monmouthshire Fire Brigade (Wales) | Cemetery Rd-Ebbw Vale-1970 C5 Cemetery Rd-Ebbw Vale-1976 **Converted to L4P-C03 Blaina-**Gwent Fire Brigade 109-MFB |
| ERA284H | | Res/T | 70 | 86 | Derbyshire Fire Service | B10 Park Rd-Ashbourne-1982 **Conv** Breathing App**T**-D02 Nottingham Rd-Derby-1986 110-FC-Merryweather-**Re-bodied** Reeves Burgess |
| ERA285H | | Res/T | 70 | 86 | Derbyshire Fire Service | C2/8 Market St-Clay Cross- **Converted into Breathing App/T by Reeves Burgess** 110-Forward Control-Reeves Burgess |
| APA91H | | O2/T BAT | 70 | ? | Surrey County Council Fire Brigade | **ex Accident Res/V-Farnham-**  ?  / Church St-Epsom 108-SCCFB |
| APA92H | | Decon Unit | 70 | 78 | Surrey County Council Fire Brigade | **ex Accident Res/V-Dorking**   ? Addlestone-Chertsey-1972/Staines Rd West-Sunbury-1978 108-SCCFB |
| APA93H | | Accident Res/V | 70 | 80 | Surrey County Council Fire Brigade | Povey Cross Rd-Horley-1974 B10 Povey Cross Rd-Horley-1978/Res-1980/West Sussex 108-SCCFB |
| APA94H | | Decon Unit | 70 | ? | Surrey County Council Fire Brigade | **ex Accident Res/V-Esher**   ?  / Guilford Rd-Farnham 108-SCCFB |
| UPM349H | | Res/T | 70 | 93 | East Sussex Fire Brigade | 7 South Rd-Haywards Heath-1974/A1 North St-Lewes-1993 109-HCB Angus |
| UPM350H | | Res/T | 70 | | East Sussex Fire Brigade | 12 Keld Ave-Uckfield-1973-**Conv L4V**-Crowborough-1984 A04 Preston Circus-Brighton 109-HCB Angus-Firestrike |
| PDL647H | | Res/T | 70 | 80 | Isle of Wight Fire Brigade | 1 South St-Newport 109-IoW FB |
| VOT334H | | Res/T | 70 | 86 | Hampshire Fire Brigade | D42 Fairmile Rd-Christchurch-1974 B26 Fairmile Rd-Christchurch-1986-Dorset Fire Brigade 109-HFS |
| RFW784H | | ET | 70 | 82 | Lindsey Fire Brigade | Churchill Ave-Skegness-1974 B1 Churchill Ave-Skegness-1982-Lincolnshire Fire Brigade 109 **LWB**-HCB Angus |
| VFW915J | | ET | 70 | 83 | Lindsey Fire Brigade | Eastfield Rd-Louth-1974 B5 Eastfield Rd-Louth-1983 -Lincolnshire Fire Brigade 109 **LWB**-Carmichael |
| VFW916J | | ET | 70 | 85 | Lindsey Fire Brigade | Nelson St-Gainsborough-1974 A2 Nelson St-Gainsborough-1985 Lincolnshire Fire Brigade 109 **LWB**-Carmichael |
| AJB760J | | Res/T | 70 | 76 | Berkshire & Reading Fire Brigade | C4 Hawthorne Rd-Newbury-1972 B2 Wokingham Rd-Reading-1975 E16 Downshire Way-Bracknell -Royal Berkshire Fire Brigade        107-Air Drive |
| RGS475J | | TS/Unit | 70 | ? | Perth & Kinross Fire Brigade (Scotland) | Kinross Fire Station 108-Carmichael |
| RAV703J | | L4P | 71 | 85 | North Eastern Area Fire Brigade (Scotland) | North Anderson Drive-Aberdeen-1975 E77 N Anderson Drive-Aberdeen-1980 **Converted Rescue Tender** E77 Aberdeen-1985-Grampian Fire Brigade-        / **L4V** 108-Carmichael |
| TSD310J | | Res/T BAT | 71 | 80 | South Western Area Fire Brigade (Scotland) | Brooms Rd-Dumfries-1975 D1 Brooms Rd-Dumfries-1980-Dumfries & Galloway FB 108-SWAFB |
| TSD311J | | Res/T BAT | 71 | 86 | South Western Area Fire Brigade (Scotland) | Titchfield St-Kilmarnock-1975 :Converted Road Rescue Unit D2 Titchfield Rd-Kilmarnock -1980 E14 Old Carlisle-Lesmahagow-1989-Strathclyde Fire Brigade   108-SWAFB |

| Reg | | Code | | | Fire Brigade | Details |
|---|---|---|---|---|---|---|
| **PXA538J** | | CRT | 71 | 88 | Fife Fire Brigade (Scotland) | Carnegie Drive-Dunfermline 109-FFB |
| **WCX111J** | | Res/T | 71 | 79 | Huddersfield County Borough Fire Brigade | Outcote Bank-Huddersfield-1974 C11 Outcote Bank-Huddersfield-1979 West Yorkshire FS 109-Pyrene |
| **NRB937J** | | LRP | 71 | 78 | Derbyshire Fire Service | B4 Chesterfield Rd-Matlock 110-Forward Control-Merryweather |
| **BAC999J** | | ET | 71 | 79 | Warwick County Fire Brigade | 31 Corporation St-Rugby-1978-Reserve-1979 110-Forward Control-Carmichael |
| **BHO206J** | | Res/T | 71 | 76 | Hampshire Fire Brigade | A3 Reading Rd-Farnborough 110-Forward Control-HCB Angus |
| **BHO207J** | | Res/T | 71 | 79 | Hampshire Fire Brigade | A1 West Ham Close-Basingstoke 110-Forward Control-HCB Angus |
| **JBJ118J** | | RAV | 72 | 79 | Suffolk & Ipswich Fire Service | B01 Fornham Rd-Bury St Edmond's 110-S&IFS |
| **GBL579K** | | Res/T | 71 | 82 | Berkshire & Reading Fire Brigade | C4 Hawthorne Rd-Newbury-1974 W4 Hawthorne Rd-Newbury-1982 Royal Berkshire FB 110-Carmichael -Air Drive |
| **VDO99K** | | ET | 71 | 87 | Holland County Fire Brigade | Church Lane-Sleaford-1974 D9 Church Lane-Sleaford-1987-Lincolnshire Fire Brigade 109 **LWB**-Carmichael |
| **VSD192K** | | Res/T BAT | 71 | 89 | South Western Area  Fire Brigade (Scotland) | Pennyburn Stevenson-Irvine Nth-1975 D3 Irvine North -**Converted Road Rescue Unit** F14  Lynwood-Arrochar-1989-Strathclyde Fire Brigade 108-SWAFB |
| **FTX947K** | | HLL | 71 | 87 | Glamorgan County Fire Brigade (Wales) | **ex L4V-   ?   /** 5 Grove Place-Swansea-1987-West Glamorgan County FS 109-CoSFB |
| **YWO386K** | | L4P | 71 | 82 | Monmouthshire Fire Brigade (Wales) | Cae White-Blaenavon-1974/B17 Cae White-Blaenavon-1978 **Converted Rescue Tender** B16 Hereford Rd-Abergavenny-1982/Gwent Fire Brigade 109-MFB |
| **YWO387K** | | Res/T | 71 | 83 | Monmouthshire Fire Brigade (Wales) | Rockfield Rd-Monmouth-1974 B14 Rockfield Rd-Monmouth-1975 B19 New Rd-New InnPontypool-1983 Gwent Fire Brigade 109-MFB |
| **BGG736K** | | RRU | 72 | 80 | Glasgow Fire Service (Scotland) | B1 South Fire Station-1980 108-Bennett |
| **REY165K** | | Res/T | 72 | | Angelsey County Borough FB (Wales) | Isgraig-Llangefni-1975/12 Isgraig-Llangefni-1978 **Converted to Control Unit** 09 Llanberis Rd-Caernarfon-Gwynedd Fire Service 108-Carmichael-GFS |
| **TPV925K** | | RAV | 72 | 79 | Suffolk & Ipswich Fire Brigade | Normanhurst Rd-Lowestoft-1974 / A14 Lowestoft-1979 Suffolk Fire Service 109-S&IFB |
| **ELV514L** | 1118 | Res/T | 72 | 83 | City of Liverpool | #10 Conleach Rd-Speke-1974/S3 Conleach Rd-Speke-1983 Merseyside Fire Brigade-**Sold to Liverpool (Speke) Airport** 110-Forward Control-CLFB |
| **YDO656L** | | ET | 72 | 86 | Holland County Fire Brigade | West Elloe Ave-Spalding-1974 C2 West Elloe Ave-Spalding-1986-Lincolnshire Fire Brigade 109 **LWB**-Carmichael |
| **NBL771L** | | Res/T | 72 | 82 | Berkshire & Reading Fire Brigade | A11 Bridge St-Maidenhead-1974 E19 Bridge St-Maidenhead-1982   Royal Berkshire FB 110-Forward Control-Carmichael |
| **SWX273L** | | Res/T | 72 | 78 | West Riding of Yorkshire Fire Brigade | South Lane-Elland-1974 B13 South Lane-Elland-1978-West Yorkshire Fire Service 109-Pyrene |
| **SWX274L** | | Res/T | 72 | 83 | West Riding of Yorkshire Fire Brigade | Knolbeck Lane-Brampton Bierlow-1974 A6 Brampton Bierlow-1978/B4 Union Rd-Thorne-1983 South Yorkshire County Fire Service          109-Pyrene |

The West Riding of Yorkshire Fire Brigade ordered fourteen Land Rover 109 Rescue Tenders in 1972 and these were fitted with Pyrene bodywork. They were delivered in a white livery that was synonymous at the time with West Riding. SWX281L was pictured in the rear yard of Goole fire station, some time after the appliance had passed to Humberside Fire Brigade control, as indicated by the crest on the door. *Norman Downs*

| | | | | | | |
|---|---|---|---|---|---|---|
| SWX275L | | Res/T | 72 | 80 | West Riding of Yorkshire Fire Brigade | Stansfield Rd-Todmorden<br>B19 Stansfield Rd-Todmorden-1980-West Yorkshire FS<br>109-Pyrene |
| SWX276L | | Res/T | 72 | 78 | West Riding of Yorkshire Fire Brigade | Beancroft Rd-Castleford-1974<br>F12 Beancroft Rd-Castleford-1978-West Yorkshire FS<br>109-Pyrene |
| SWX277L | | Res/T | 72 | 79 | West Riding of Yorkshire Fire Brigade | Keighley Rd-Bingley-1974<br>A12 Keighley Rd-Bingley-1979-West Yorkshire FS<br>109-Pyrene |
| SWX278L | | Res/T | 72 | 79 | West Riding of Yorkshire Fire Brigade | New St-Slaithwaite-1974<br>C20 New St-Slaithwaite-1979-West Yorkshire Fire Service<br>109-Pyrene |
| SWX279L | | Res/T | 72 | 85 | West Riding of Yorkshire Fire Brigade | Hazel Rd-Knottingley-1974<br>F15 Hazel Rd-Knottingley-1982<br>F18 Stuart Rd-Pontefract-1985-West Yorkshire Fire Service<br>109-Pyrene |
| SWX280L | | Res/T | 72 | 80 | West Riding of Yorkshire Fire Brigade | A11 Skipton Rd-Harrogate-1974<br>A1 Skipton Rd-Harrogate-1980-North Yorkshire Fire Brigade       109-Pyrene |
| SWX281L | | Res/T | 72 | 93 | West Riding of Yorkshire Fire Brigade | B14 Larsen Rd-Goole-1974<br>D2 Larsen Rd-Goole-1976<br>B3 Bessingby Rd-Bridlington-1989<br>A4 New Walkergate-Beverley-1993-Humberside Fire Brigade       109-Pyrene |
| SWX282L | | Res/T | 72 | 85 | West Riding of Yorkshire Fire Brigade | Walton Rd-Wetherby-1974<br>D16 Walton Rd-Wetherby-1982-Training School-1985<br>West Yorkshire Fire Service<br>109-Pyrene |
| SWX283L | | Res/T | 72 | 82 | West Riding of Yorkshire Fire Brigade | Hightown Rd-Cleckheaton-1974<br>C13 Hightown Rd-Cleckheaton-1982-West Yorkshire FS<br>109-Pyrene |
| SWX284L | | Res/T | 72 | 82 | West Riding of Yorkshire Fire Brigade | Corporation St-Morley-Leeds-1974<br>E14 Corporation St-Morley-1982-West Yorkshire FS<br>109-Pyrene |
| SWX285L | | Res/T | 72 | 83 | West Riding of Yorkshire Fire Brigade | Quarry Lane-Adwick le Street-1974<br>B2 Quarry Lane-Adwick le St-1983<br>South Yorkshire County FS<br>109-Pyrene |
| SWX286L | | Res/T | 72 | 88 | West Riding of Yorkshire Fire Brigade | E23 Broughton Rd-Skipton-1974<br>A8 Broughton Rd-Skipton-1981 -**Goathland Vol-NYFB-1988**       109-Pyrene |
| HUE999L | | ET | 73 | 85 | Warwick County Fire Brigade | 23 Park Rd-Coleshill-1976<br>51 Masons Ave Stratford on Avon-1985<br>110-Forward Control-Carmichael |
| KCY261L | | Res/T | 73 | 83 | City of Swansea (Wales) | Snay Rd-Morriston-Swansea-1974<br>8 Snay Rd-Morriston-1983-West Glamorgan County FS<br>109-HCB Angus-**White Livery** |
| DAG332L | | Res/T<br>BAT | 73 | | South Western Area Fire Brigade (Scotland) | Arthur St-Newton Stewart-1975<br>B6 Arthur St-Newton Stewart-1980-Dumfries & Galloway FB       108-SWAFB |
| DWV260L | | FOT | 73 | | Wiltshire Fire Brigade | 3/1 Ashley Rd-Sailsbury<br>**L4V Headquarters-1990-L4V-3/4 Mere-**<br>109-WFB |
| NGL999L | | Res/T | 73 | 85 | City of Bath | Cleveland Bridge-Bath-1974<br>B1 Cleveland Bridge-Bath-1985   County of Avon FB<br>110 Forward Control-Carmichael |
| NWW643M | | Res/T | 73 | 80 | West Riding of Yorkshire Fire Brigade | Little Lane-Ilkley-1974<br>A16 Little Lane-Ilkley-1980 -West Yorkshire Fire Service<br>109-Chubb |

| | | | | | | |
|---|---|---|---|---|---|---|
| OGD142M | | RRU | 74 | 83 | Glasgow Fire Service (Scotland) | C3 Partick Fire Station-1975<br>F63 Bunessan- 1983-Strathclyde Fire Brigade<br>**Converted to L4P**<br>108-Bennett |
| TOU767M | | Res/T | 74 | 81 | Hampshire Fire Brigade | B17 West St-Fareham<br>110-Forward Control-HCB Angus |
| TOU768M | | Res/T | 74 | 81 | Hampshire Fire Brigade | D53 Redbridge Hill-Southampton<br>110-Forward Control-HCB Angus |
| UYD589M | | Cliff/RU | 74 | | Somerset Fire Brigade | **ex HRT-  ?** / A04 Marine Drive-Burnham on Sea<br>109-Somerset FB |
| SDF892N | | Lighting Unit | 74 | 86 | Gloucestershire Fire Service | 07 Pagenhill Lane-Stroud<br>109-Bates |
| SDF893N | | Cliff/RU | 74 | 93 | Gloucestershire Fire Service | **ex L4P-  ?** / 02 Cinder Hill-Coleford<br>109-Bates |
| LWC620P | | Res/T | 76 | 81 | Essex County Fire Brigade | D84 Debden Rd-Newport-**Sold Cork County-Irish Republic**                                        109-HCB Angus |
| LWC621P | | Res/T | 76 | 81 | Essex County Fire Brigade | D70 Fourth Ave-Harlow-**Sold Cork County-Irish Republic**<br>109-HCB Angus |
| LWC622P | | Res/T | 76 | 81 | Essex County Fire Brigade | A10 Cowdrey Ave-Colchester-**Sold Cork County-Ireland**<br>109-HCB Angus |
| KPX236P | | Res/T | 76 | | Hampshire Fire Brigade | C29 Steele Close-Eastleigh-1977/A14 Swan St-Petersfield<br>109-HFB |
| MKH719P | | Res/T | 76 | 85 | Humberside Fire Brigade | B1 Southcoates Rd-Hull East<br>109-Anglo |
| MKH720P | | Res/T | 76 | 92 | Humberside Fire Brigade | A4 Albert Terrace-Beverley-1983<br>A4 New Walkergate-Beverley-1989-Reserve-1992<br>109-Anglo |
| KDW597P | | Res/T | 76 | | Gwent Fire Brigade-**1996**<br>South Wales Fire Service (Wales) | C05 Cemetery Rd-Ebbw Vale-1981<br>**Converted to L4P-B17/39 Blaenavon**<br>109-GFB |
| KDW598P | | Res/T | 76 | | Gwent Fire Brigade-**1996**<br>South Wales Fire Service (Wales) | C01 Darren Drive-Abercarn-1981 /**Converted to L4P**<br>B14 Rockfield Rd-Monmouth-1985/C03 High St-Blaina<br>109-GFB |
| KDW599P | | Res/T | 76 | 95 | Gwent Fire Brigade (Wales) | B13 Regent Way-Chepstow-1977 /**Converted to L4P**<br>C01 Darren Drive-Abercarn-1983/C08 New Park Rd-Risca<br>109-GFB |
| OJC285S | | L4P | 77 | 96 | Gwynedd Fire Service (Wales) | 16 Arran Rd-Dolgellau-1978<br>**Converted Light Rescue Pump**-16 Arran Rd-Dolgellau<br>110-Forward Control-Carmichael |
| PEY238S | | LRP | 78 | 96 | Gwynedd Fire Service (Wales) | 12 Ilsgraig-Llangefni<br>110-Forward Control-Carmichael |
| PEY239S | | LRP | 78 | 96 | Gwynedd Fire Service (Wales) | 09 Llanberis Rd-Caernarfon<br>110-Forward Control-Carmichael |
| VNO24S | | Res/T | 78 | 81 | Essex County Fire Brigade | D72 Old Station Rd-Loughton-**Sold Cork County-Ireland**<br>109-HCB Angus |
| VNO25S | | Res/T | 78 | 81 | Essex County Fire Brigade | C50 Hogg Lane-Grays-**Sold Cork County-Irish Republic**<br>109-HCB Angus |
| VNO26S | | Res/T | 78 | 88 | Essex County Fire Brigade | B34 Rainsford Lane-Chelmsford<br>**Converted to Breathing AppT**-Brigade Headquarters-1988<br>109-HCB Angus-**Re-bodied Reeves Burgess** |
| EAF517V | | Cliff/RU | 80 | | Cornwall County Fire Brigade | **ex L4T  ?** / A5 Tregunnel Hill<br>109-Eagle |
| OVV498V | | CIU | 80 | | Northamptonshire Fire Brigade | A12 Newton Rd-Rushden<br>109-NFB |
| FPO22X | A00191 | CS/Unit | 82 | | West Sussex Fire Brigade | Headquarters<br>109-WSFB |

| | | | | | | | |
|---|---|---|---|---|---|---|---|
| FVR55Y | | LRV | 83 | | Greater Manchester County Fire Service | C32 Middleton Rd-Heywood- 110-Mountain Range | ? /-L4V |
| FVR56Y | | LRV | 83 | | Greater Manchester County Fire Service | E57 Railway St-Hyde 110-Mountain Range | ? /-L4V |
| B169XHY | | HLL | 85 | | County of Avon Fire Brigade | A2 Southmead Rd-Southmead-Bristol 109-CoAFB | |
| B999EKU | | FCU | 85 | | Derbyshire Fire Service | B01 Campton Grove-Buxton 110-DFS | |
| C125ETG | | SRT | 86 | | South Glamorgan Fire & Rescue-**1996** South Wales Fire Service (Wales) | 05 Port Road East-Barry 127-Hoskins | |
| D566FJT | | Res/T | 86 | | Dorset Fire Brigade | A07 North Quay-Weymouth 110-FSE-Leicester Carriage Builders | |
| D403ERU | | Res/T | 86 | 90 | Dorset Fire Brigade | B18 Wimborne Rd-Poole/**Written off in RTA** 110-FSE-Leicester Carriage Builders | |
| D960VTN | 223 | RAV | 87 | | Durham County Fire Brigade | S9 Central Ave-Newton Aycliffe-**1991 Converted L4V** S4 Watling St-Bishop Auckland 127-Pilcher Greene | |
| E669JOU | | Rail/RU | 88 | | County of Avon Fire Brigade-**1996** Avon Fire Brigade | A07 Station Rd-Yate **Trailer tow's Rail Cart Converted L4V ex C1 Weston super Mare** 110-AFB-Permaquip | |
| F326PPG | A00190 | CS/Unit | 89 | | West Sussex Fire Brigade | C16 Oakfield Approach East Wittering 110-WSFB | |
| G987YBX | | L4R | 89 | | Dyfed Fire Brigade-**1996** Mid & West Wales FB (Wales) | A2/W02 Lime Grove Ave-Carmarthen 110-DFB | |
| N265DBF | 265 | C/Unit | 95 | | Staffordshire Fire & Rescue Service | Headquarters-Pirehall Defender 110-Rover | |
| N803BJK | | RR/Unit | 96 | | East Sussex County Fire Brigade | 22 Beeching Rd-Bexhill Defender 110-Rover | |
| P685BUX | 15 | IC/Unit | 97 | | Shropshire Fire & Rescue Service | St Michael's St-Shrewsbury Defender 110-Rover | |

| | | | | | **Range Rover Carmichael Chassied Appliances** | **The chassis was lengthened at the Carmichael works at Worcester. An extra trailing axle was added to the 4x4 makeup of the vehicle. The power was provided by a 3.5 V8 Rover petrol engine. It was also fitted with a 200gpm (909 Lpm) Godiva pump and a 200gal (909L) water tank. Some carried a small extension ladder.** |
|---|---|---|---|---|---|---|
| RPG78L | | Accident Res/V | 72 | 83 | Surrey County Council Fire Brigade | N27 London Rd-Camberley |
| BTM81L | | Res/T | 73 | 87 | Bedfordshire Fire Service | 2 Brewers Hill Rd-Dunstable-1983 13 Stopsley Way-Luton-1987 |
| BTM82L | | Res/T | 73 | 87 | Bedfordshire Fire Service | 1 Barkers Lane-Bedford-1982 5 Chestnut Way-Biggleswade-1987 |
| BTM83L | | Res/T | 73 | 87 | Bedfordshire Fire Service | 5 Chestnut Way-Biggleswade-1982 1 Barkers Lane-Bedford-1987 |
| BTM84L | | Res/T | 73 | 87 | Bedfordshire Fire Service | 10 Dunstable Rd-Toddington-1975 0 Luton Rd-Luton-1984 2 Brewers Hill-Dunstable-1987 |
| SYC124L | | L6P | 73 | 92 | Somerset Fire Brigade | A03 St Cuthberts-Dulverton |
| TEY188L | | L6P | 73 | ? | Angelsey County Borough FB (Wales) | Kingsland Rd-Holyhead-1974-**Converted Rescue Pump** Kingsland Rd-Holyhead-Gwynedd Fire Brigade |
| UST321L | | L6P | 73 | 92 | Northern Area Fire Brigade (Scotland) | Harbour Rd-Inverness-1975 A1 Harbour Rd-Inverness -Highlands & Islands FB |
| OWO490M | | Res/T | 73 | 86 | Monmouthshire Fire Brigade (Wales) | New Rd-New Inn-Pontypool-1975 B19 New Rd-New Inn-Pontypool-1977 B09 Malpas Rd-Malpas-1981-**Converted to L6P** Reserve-1986 -Gwent Fire Brigade |

**HUE999L was new to the Warwick County Fire Brigade in 1973, when it replaced an earlier Land Rover 88 Series Emergency Tender of 1958 vintage. It is a Land Rover 110 forward control Emergency Tender, and was photographed outside the Masons Avenue fire station in Stratford-on-Avon. There were four of this type of appliance delivered to Warwickhire, the others serving at Nuneaton, Rugby and Coleshill**. *Mike Bunn*

| OET72M | | Res/T | 73 | ? | Rotherham County Borough Fire Brigade | Erskine Rd-Rotherham-1974 Erskine Rd-Rotherham-South Yorkshire CFS |
|---|---|---|---|---|---|---|
| PET193M | | BAT | 74 | ? | Rotherham County Borough Fire Brigade | Oaks Lane-Rotherham-1982 Reserve-South Yorkshire CFS |
| OTD240M | 200 | Res/T | 73 | 88 | Lancashire County Fire Brigade | B34/C54 Weldbank Rd-Chorley **4x4** |
| PTJ698M | 205 | Res/T | 73 | 84 | Lancashire County Fire Brigade | E72 Manchester Rd-Mossley-1974 E56 Manchester Rd-Mossley-1984 -Greater Manchester CFS |
| PTJ699M | 206 | Res/T | 73 | 83 | Lancashire County Fire Brigade | E77 Middleton Rd-Heywood-1974 C32 Middleton Rd-Heywood-1983-Greater Manchester CFS |

| | | | | | | |
|---|---|---|---|---|---|---|
| SUR75M | | ERT | 73 | 86 | Hertfordshire County Council Fire Brigade | A10 St Albans Rd-Garston-1985 |
| TPO513M | | Res/T | 74 | 93 | West Sussex Fire Brigade | A17 Northgate-Chichester |
| TPO514M | A00005 | Res/T | 74 | | West Sussex Fire Brigade | B12 Hurst Rd-Horsham |
| HAF481N | | L6P | 74 | 91 | Cornwall County Fire Brigade | A8 North St-Redruth-1980 B16 Townsend-Polruan-1991- **Preserved** |
| JKG887N | | Res/T | 75 | ? | Mid Glamorgan Fire Brigade (Wales) | 01 Sunnyside-Bridgend |
| KMJ969N | | Res/T | 75 | 90 | Bedfordshire Fire Service | 10 Dunstable Rd-Toddington-1987 5 Chestnut Ave-Biggleswade-1990 |
| XPD291N | | Accident Res/V | 75 | 89 | Surrey County Council Fire Brigade | W29 Church St-Woking |
| XPD292N | | Accident Res/V | 75 | 89 | Surrey County Council Fire Brigade | E10 Croydon Rd-Reigate |
| LKX968P | | ERT | 75 | | Hertfordshire County Council Fire Brigade | B18 Wellfield Rd-Hatfield-1985 A10 St Albans Rd-Garston- |
| KMR673P | | Res/T | 76 | 90 | Wiltshire Fire Brigade | 2/1 Dallas Rd-Chippenham **Donated to Romania** |
| KBP550P | | Res/T | 76 | 93 | West Sussex Fire Brigade | A01 Ardsheal Rd-Worthing Reserve- |
| LDW640P | | Res/T | 76 | 84 | Mid Glamorgan Fire Brigade (Wales) | 21 Dynevor Street-Merthyr Tydfil |
| OUY316P | | Res/T | 76 | 90 | Hereford & Worcester Fire Brigade | W46 Owen St-Hereford-1980 E25 Windsor St-Bromsgrove-1990 |
| RNP186P | | Res/T | 76 | 90 | Hereford & Worcester Fire Brigade | E21 Copenhagen St-Worcester-1978 E25 Windsor St-Bromsgrove-1980 W46 Owen St-Hereford-1990 |
| NCC777R | | L6R | 76 | 88 | County of Clwyd Fire Service (Wales) | E2 Chester Rd-Deeside |
| NCC778R | | L6R | 76 | 88 | County of Clwyd Fire Service (Wales) | W1 Coast Rd-Rhyl |
| PNU999R | | Res/T | 76 | 88 | Nottinghamshire Fire Brigade | 12 Wharf Rd-Retford |
| YAU705S | | Res/T | 78 | 88 | Nottinghamshire Fire Brigade | 05 Sutton Rd-Kirkby in Ashfield |
| DMB67S | | Res/T | 78 | 89 | Cheshire County Fire Brigade | B6 Ordenance Ave-Birchwood |
| DMB68S | | Res/T | 78 | 89 | Cheshire County Fire Brigade | B3 Mobberley Rd-Knutsford |
| TAX779S | | Res/T | 78 | 86 | Mid Glamorgan Fire Brigade (Wales) | 15 Oxford St-Pontypridd |
| THN949S | | Res/T | 78 | 90 | Cleveland County Fire Brigade | 09 Stranton-West Hartlepool |
| DRA982T | | Res/T | 79 | 89 | Nottinghamshire Fire Brigade | 126 Boundary Rd-Newark |
| | | | | | | The appliances listed below are all 4x4 non Carmichael bodied. |
| A782SUL | AFC-1/LR-2 | FCU | 84 | 94 | London Fire Brigade | South East Area-Reserve |
| D895FYM | AFC-2/LR-5 | FCU | 86 | 95 | London Fire Brigade | North East Area-Romford Rd-Stratford |
| D896FYM | AFC-3/LR-6 | FCU | 86 | 95 | London Fire Brigade | South East Area-High St-Lewisham |
| D897FYM | AFC-4/LR-7 | FCU | 86 | 95 | London Fire Brigade | North Area-Harrow Rd-Paddington |
| D898FYM | AFC-5/LR-8 | FCU | 86 | 95 | London Fire Brigade | North West Area-Pinner Rd-Harrow |
| D899FYM | AFC-6/LR-9 | FCU | 86 | 95 | London Fire Brigade | South West Area-Old Town-Clapham |
| D751PPP | | C/Unit | 87 | | Essex County Fire & Rescue Service | Brigade Headquarters |
| K652WPE | | FCU | 92 | | Surrey Fire & Rescue Service | Brigade Headquarters |

Carmichael's of Worcester supplied all bodying associated with the Range Rover 3.5V8 chassis. The Rescue/Emergency Tender variant, used extensively in the 1970s, proved particularly popular and representing the type is LKX968P which served Hatfield in Hertfordshire. The trailing third axle was added to take the additional weight of the equipment carried. *Michael Lawmon.*

| | | | | | Reynolds Boughton Chassied Appliances | |
|---|---|---|---|---|---|---|
| JBG513P | 1131 | CRT | 75 | 82 | Merseyside Fire Brigade | Liverpool Speke Airport Pathfinder-Chubb |
| JPO646P | | Res/T | 76 | 90 | West Sussex Fire Brigade | B08 Ifield Ave-Crawley-1990 **Sold to Redhill Aerodrome** Persuer-Chubb |
| XKB925W | 1195 | CRT | 81 | 82 | Merseyside Fire Brigade | Liverpool Speke Airport RB44-Carmichael |
| YAG470X | | Res/T | 81 | 89 | Humberside Fire Brigade | A3 Calvert Lane-Hull West RB44-Angloco |
| A319NRH | | Res/T | 83 | 95 | Humberside Fire Brigade | D2 Larsen Rd-Goole RB44-Merryweather |
| A700RYA | | Res/T | 84 | 93 | Somerset Fire Brigade | 01 Lisieux Way-Taunton RB44-Saxon |
| A512MRW | | Res/T | 84 | 89 | Warwick County Fire Brigade | SD35 Masons Ave-Stratford on Avon RB44-Carmichael |
| A513MRW | | Res/T | 84 | 89 | Warwick County Fire Brigade | ND22 Park Rd-Coleshill RB44-Carmichael |
| C382HCA | | ERT | 85 | 90 | Hertfordshire County Council Fire Brigade | B18 Wellfield Rd-Hatfield RB44-Saxon |

**Crawley fire station ran JPO646P, a Reynolds Boughton/Chubb Crash Tender for many years. Gatwick Airport, for which a foam capibility was required, is within Crawley's area. In 1990 this appliance was replaced by a crash tender based on a Mercedes-Benz, allowing JPO646P to continue in a aircraft firefighting role at Redhill Aerodrome in Surrey. Interesting is the rare type of beacon on the roof.** *Michael Lawmon*

| | | | | | Stonefield P5000<br>Chassied Appliances | The short lived Scottish firm of Stonefield Vehicles Ltd was set up to produce a unique types of 4x4 and 6x4 specialist vehicles. They were powered by a 5.2 litre V8 petrol engine. |
|---|---|---|---|---|---|---|
| CKH964T | | Res/T | 78 | 83 | Humberside Fire Brigade | D2 Larsen Rd-Goole<br>Body work-Angloco |
| GDS85T | | E/Support Unit | 79 | 88 | Strathclyde Fire Brigade (Scotland) | F01 Kilbowie Rd-Hardgate-Clydebank<br>Body work-Fulton & Wylie |
| DEB896V | | Res/T | 80 | 89 | Cambridgeshire Fire & Rescue Service | B01 Parkside-Cambridge-1985<br>A20 Churhill Way-Wisbech-1989<br>Body work-CMC |
| BVA9V | | Res/T | 80 | 88 | Cambridgeshire Fire & Rescue Service | A14 Dogsthorpe Rd-Peterborough<br>Body work-CMC |
| FSO662V | | ET Foam/C | 80 | 92 | Grampian Fire Brigade (Scotland) | N37 Friars Rd-Elgin-1990<br>**Converted to Cliff Rescue Unit**<br>E77 North Anderson Drive-Aberdeen<br>Body work-Grampian FB |
| TSF706V | | ET L6P | 80 | 87 | Lothian & Borders Fire Brigade (Scotland) | 34 Abbotsford Rd-Galashiels<br>Body work-Fulton & Wylie |

BVA9V, a Stonefield P5000 with 6x4 wheel drive, was one of two operated by the Cambridgeshire Fire & Rescue Service. This vehicle was based at Dogsthorpe Rd, Peterborough, while the other was located at Parkside, Cambridge. Stonefield appliances are rare with only six examples seeing service with United Kingdom brigades. However, many have found roles with airport fire services.
*Michael Lawmon*

An example of the Shelvoke & Drewry WX chassis is A806AWP, shown here with HCB Angus bodywork. This Evesham-based water appliance served many years at Ross-on-Wye in Herefordshire before moving to Worcestershire following the amalgamation of the two counties. The water tank has a capacity of 4546 litres and the vehicle also has its own built in fire pump. *Clive Shearman*

# SHELVOKE & DREWRY

| Reg No | Fleet No | TYPE | YR | OS | Appliance & Brigade Name | Details/Stations |
|---|---|---|---|---|---|---|
| | | | | | **Shelvoke & Drewry Chassied Specialist Appliances** | **WY series chassis, assembled by the Special Purpose Division of S&D Ltd were ideal for the larger Aerial machines. Available in 13.5 or 16 ton variants.** |
| POB983R | 086 Q69VOE 085 | ET/CU BAT | 77 | 88 | West Midlands Fire Service | B1 Radford Rd-Coventry-1979 B4 Sir Henry Parkes Rd-Canley-1988-**Converted into PRL** WX-Benson |
| POB984R | 102 Q68VOE/086 | ET/CU BAT | 77 | 88 | West Midlands Fire Service | D1 Old Park Lane-Oldbury-1988-**Converted into PRL** WX-Benson |
| POB985R | 107 Q67VOE 087 | ET/CU BAT | 77 | 88 | West Midlands Fire Service | A1 Lancaster Circus-1979 A2 Ettington Rd-Aston-1988-**Converted into PRL** WX-Angloco |
| UOF638S | 252 Q70VOE 089 | ET/CU BAT | 77 | 88 | West Midlands Fire Service | C5 Pershore Rd South-Kings Norton **Converted into PRL** WX-Benson |
| NTN877R RRG378S | | Res/T | 77 | 87 | Tyne & Wear Metropolitan FB | T Victoria Rd-Hebburn-1981 / F Fossway-Newcastle-1987 **Written off in RTA** WX-Carmichael |
| UTW421W | | MRT | 81 | 95 | Essex County Fire & Rescue Service | A10 Cowdray Ave-Colchester WX-Pilcher Greene |
| UTW422W | | MRT | 81 | 95 | Essex County Fire & Rescue Service | C50 Hogg Lane-Grays WX-Pilcher Greene |
| UTW423W | | MRT | 81 | 95 | Essex County Fire & Rescue Service | D70 Fourth Ave-Harlow-1991-Reserve-1995 WX-Pilcher Greene |
| ETN909W | | Res/T | 81 | 94 | Tyne & Wear Metropolitan FB | T Victoria Rd-Hebburn-1988/F Fossway-Newcastle-1989 D Pilgrim St-Newcastle Central-1994/**Preserved** WX-Carmichael |
| EBB847W | | FOT | 81 | 95 | Tyne & Wear Metropolitan FB | H York Rd-Whitley Bay-1993/Reserve-1995 WX-Chubb |
| KOG242W | 123 Q66VOE-090 | FOT | 81 | 88 | West Midlands Fire Service | D7 Alexander Rd-Tipton-1988-**Converted into PRL** WX-Angloco |
| VDV143X | | BAT | 81 | | Suffolk Fire Service | **ex TL Torquay-Devon F&RS-1988** A01 Colchester Rd-Ipswich WY-SFS |
| A806AWP | | WRC | 84 | | Hereford & Worcester Fire Brigade | **ex WD44 Ross on Wye-1993** CD28 Merstowe Place-Evesham- WX-HCB Angus |
| B128CVH | W628 | ET | 85 | | Hertfordshire County Council Fire Brigade | **ex WRL Potters Bar-1993**/Reserve- WX-Angloco |
| | | | | | **Shelvoke & Drewry Turntable Ladders** | **The 16 Ton WY chassis proved an ideal platform for aerial appliances.** Due to an accident in Cornwall a large number of re chassied Merryweather ladders were inspected and ultimately withdrawn. |
| XGG731S | | TL | 78 | 89 | Strathclyde Fire Brigade (Scotland) | F1 Kilbowie Rd-Clydebank **L Re-ch off Bedford TK-UMS197-Central Region FB** Carmichael-Magirus DL30-100'L |
| XGG732S | | TL | 78 | 93 | Strathclyde Fire Brigade (Scotland) | A3 Petershill Rd-Springburn-Glasgow D2 Campbell St-Kilmarnock **L Re-chassied off Commer-OSD558-South Western AFB** Carmichael-Magirus DL30-100'L |
| WVE742T | | TL | 79 | 84 | Cambridgeshire Fire & Rescue Service | B1 Parkside-Cambridge-1984-**Written off in RTA** Benson-Metz-DLK30-104'L |

This Shelvoke & Drewry WY chassis-based turntable ladder served out of the Parkside station in Cambridge for five years. It was withdrawn following an accident. This shape of cab / chassis was used only on three Aerial Ladders, the other two being supplied to the to Strathclyde Fire Brigade.
*Mike Bunn*

West Midlands Fire Service operated four Shelvoke & Drewry WX models as emergency tender/control units. Seen here at Kings Norton is UOF638S while the others were stationed at Coventry, Oldbury and Central in Birmingham. They served for almost eleven years before being refurbished and re-bodied as pump rescue ladders.
*Michael Lawmon*

| | | | | | | |
|---|---|---|---|---|---|---|
| PGB355V | | TL | 80 | 92 | Strathclyde Fire Brigade (Scotland) | A7 Kelvinhaugh St-West-Glasgow<br>F&Wylie-Pierreville-100'L |
| PGA310V | | TL | 80 | 93 | Strathclyde Fire Brigade (Scotland) | E1 Bothwell Rd-Hamilton<br>F&Wylie-Pierreville-100'L |
| NHS992V | | TL | 80 | 94 | Strathclyde Fire Brigade (Scotland) | B1 South Fire Station-Glasgow<br>B5 Calder St-Polmadie-Glasgow<br>**Ladders Re-chassied off AEC Mercury-514BGE**<br>G&T Power-Merryweather-100'L |
| NHS993V | | TL | 80 | 93 | Strathclyde Fire Brigade (Scotland) | C4 Canal St-Paisley-1987-Training School-1993<br>**Ladders Re-chassied off AEC Mercury-RHS180**<br>G&T Power-Merryweather-100'L |
| GRJ297V | | TL | 80 | 94 | Greater Manchester County Fire Service | **ex D40 Whitehill St-Stockport-1987** Reserve-1994<br>Carmichael-Magirus-DL30-100'L |
| NTA750W | | TL | 81 | 92 | Devon Fire Brigade | 32 Howell Rd-Exeter-1983<br>02 Marlborough Rd-Ilfracombe-1992<br>**Ladders Re-chassied off AEC Mercury-BFJ777B**<br>G&T Power-Merryweather-100'L |
| NTA751W | | TL | 81 | 92 | Devon Fire Brigade | 50 Greenbank-Plymouth-1985 /Training School-1992<br>**Ladders Re-chassied off AEC Mercury-VJY44**<br>G&T Power-Merryweather-100'L |
| PNW625W | | TL | 81 | 91 | West Yorkshire Fire Service | C Div Skircoat Moor Rd-Halifax<br>**Ladders Re-chassied off AEC Mercury-MJX470**<br>G&T Power-Merryweather-100'L |
| VDV143X | | TL | 82 | 93 | Devon Fire Brigade | 17 Newton Rd-Torquay-1992/**Sold to Suffolk FB**<br>A2 Princes St-Ipswich-1993<br>A01 Colchester Rd-Ipswich-Date<br>**Ladders Re-chassied off AEC Mercury-CTA297C**<br>**Chassis used for Breathing Apparatus Unit**<br>G&T Power-Merryweather-100'L |
| ANO169X | | TL | 82 | 94 | Essex County Fire Brigade | D70 Fourth Ave-Harlow<br>**Ladders Re-chassied off AEC Mercury-6708EV**<br>**Ladders removed/used for HGV**<br>G&T Power-Merryweather-100'L |
| YVN67Y ' | | TL | 82 | 94 | North Yorkshire Fire Brigade | **ex W1 Skipton Rd-Harrogate-1988-Reserve-Date**<br>**Ladders Re-chassied off AEC Mercury-OVY200**<br>G&T Power-Merryweather-100'L |
| VRC995Y | | TL | 83 | 90 | Derbyshire Fire Service | **ex D03 Kingsway-Derby-1985**<br>A01 Derby Rd-Ilkeston-1990<br>**Ladders Re-chassied off AEC Mercury-BCH123B**<br>G&T Power-Merryweather-100'L |
| CDV78Y | | TL | 83 | 94 | Devon Fire Brigade | **ex 32 Howells Rd-Exeter-1992**<br>02 Marlborough Rd-Ilfracombe-1994<br>**Written off in RTA**<br>Angloco-Metz-DLK30U-100'L |
| NYL712Y | | TL | 83 | | Fire Service College | Moreton in Marsh-Gloucestershire<br>Carmichael-Magirus DL30E 100'L |
| A52CTV | | TL | 84 | | Nottinghamshire Fire Brigade | 18 Shakespeare St-Nottingham<br>Angloco-Metz DLK30U 100'L |
| A318ASF | | TL | 84 | | Lothian & Borders Fire Brigade (Scotland) | 51 Telford Rd-Crewe Toll-Edingburgh<br>Angloco-Metz DLK30U-100'L |
| A344MVX | | TL | 84 | 94 | Essex County Fire Brigade | B34 Rainsford Lane-Chelmsford<br>**Ladders Re-chassied off AEC Mercury-750SWC**<br>G&T Power-Merryweather-100'L |
| B998KTV | | TL | 85 | | Derbyshire Fire Service | D03 Kingsway-Derby<br>Carmichael-Magirus DL30E 100'L |
| B999KTV | | TL | 85 | | Derbyshire Fire Service | **ex B3 Glossop-1990/Reserve**<br>Carmichael-Magirus DL30E 100'L |

| | | Shelvoke & Drewry<br>Chassied Hydraulic Platforms | | | | |
|---|---|---|---|---|---|---|
| OYS620V | | HP | 80 | ? | Strathclyde Fire Brigade | Booms Re-ch off AEC Mercury-513BGE<br>WY- Simon SS65 |
| HOP539W | 125 | HP | 80 | | West Midlands Fire Service | ex E5 Merridale Rd-Wolverhampton  1994<br>Reserve-1995 / B2Garretts Green Lane-Sheldon-<br>WY-Angloco-Simon SS263 |
| GYW663W | HP3 | HP | 81 | | GLC London Fire Brigade | ex K28/H38 Sutton-1985<br>ex F41 Rainham Rd-Dagenham-1990/East Reserve -<br>WY-CFE-Simon SS220 |
| GYW664W | HP4 | HP | 81 | 95 | GLC London Fire Brigade | H Division/South West Area Training<br>Booms re-chassied onto<br>Volvo FL6-18 Angloco-N991OHV -HP 19  (H43)<br>WY-CFE-Simon SS220 |
| GYW665W | HP5 | HP | 81 | 95 | GLC London Fire Brigade | ex A27/G33 Chelsea-1985/North East Area Training<br>Booms re-chassied onto<br>Volvo FL6-18  Saxon-N992OHV-HP 20 (E22)<br>WY-CFE-Simon SS220 |
| GYW666W | HP6 | HP | 81 | 94 | GLC London Fire Brigade | ex A28/G33  Old Court-Kensington-1985<br>ex J25/A33 Loys Rd-Tottenham-1991<br>North Area Training Centre-1994<br>Written off in RTA<br>WY-CFE-Simon SS220 |
| GYW667W | HP7 | HP | 81 | 95 | GLC London Fire Brigade | ex J25/A33 Tottenham-1985<br>B31/H25 Norwood Rd-West Norwood<br>Booms Re-chassied Volvo FL6-18-K959EYH (HP 18)<br>WY-CFE-Simon SS220 |
| GYW668W | HP8 | HP | 81 | 95 | GLC London Fire Brigade | ex A21 Paddington-1985/North East Area Training<br>WY-CFE-Simon SS220 |
| GYW669W | HP9 | HP | 81 | 92 | GLC London Fire Brigade | ex K22/H33 Wandsworth-1985/ex G30 Wembley-1992<br>NW Training -1995/ Severely Fire Damaged-1995<br>Booms Rechassied Volvo FL6-18 -P462RHV (HP22)<br>WY-CFE-Simon SS220 |
| KUV695X | HP10 | HP | 82 | 95 | GLC London Fire Brigade | K31/H41 Richmond Rd-Richmond<br>Booms Rechassied Volvo FL6-18-P463RHV  (HP23)<br>WY-CFE-Simon SS220 |
| KUV696X | HP11 | HP | 82 | | GLC London Fire Brigade | ex F22 Poplar-1991/ C22/F31 Kingsland Rd-Kingsland-<br>H43  South Rd-Twickenham-1996/West Reserve-<br>WY-CFE-Simon SS220 |
| KUV697X | HP12 | HP | 82 | 95 | GLC London Fire Brigade | ex C22/F31 Kingsland-1991<br>ex J25/A33 Tottenham-1992/Reserve-1995<br>Booms re-chassied onto<br>Volvo FL6-18 Saxon-N993OHV-HP 21<br>WY-CFE-Simon SS220 |
| LNY617X | | HP | 81 | | Gwent Fire Brigade -1996<br>South Wales Fire Service (Wales) | B11 Archibald St-Maindee-Newport-1993<br>B20/32  Henlly's Way-Cwmbran-<br>WY-Angloco-Simon SS263 |
| KYY295X | | HP | 81 | | Fire Service College | FSC Moreton in Marsh-Gloucestershire<br>WY-Angloco-Simon SS220 |
| NOV870X | 136 | HP | 82 | | West Midlands Fire Service | ex D1 Oldbury-1992/B1 Streetsbrook Rd-Solihull<br>WY-Acoma-Simon SS263 |
| VDV144X | | HP | 82 | 93 | Devon Fire Brigade | 48 Ferndale Rd-Camels Head-1991<br>02 Marlborough Rd-Ilfracombe-1993<br>Booms off  Leyland Beaver-Carmichael-HCO999F<br>WY-Benson-Simon SS65 |
| BVM543Y | | HP | 82 | | Greater Manchester County<br>Fire Service | ex A15 Stretford-1991/Reserve-Date<br>WY-Angloco-Simon SS263 |
| WDP169Y | | HP | 83 | | Royal Berkshire Fire & Rescue<br>Service | ex A01 Caversham Rd-Reading-1989<br>17 Tuns Lane-Slough<br>WY-Angloco-Simon SS263 |

| DVC274Y | HP1 | HP | 84 | | Warwick County Fire Brigade | SD 29 Warwick St-Royal Leamington Spa<br>WY-HCB Angus-Simon SS263 |
|---------|-----|-----|----|----|-----|-----|
| A260JMS | | HP | 83 | 95 | Central Region Fire Brigade<br>(Scotland) | S8 Rannoch Rd-Stirling-1993/Reserve-1995<br>**Booms off ERF 84RS-F&Wylie-Simon SS85-PMS224G**<br>WY-F&Wylie-Simon SS85 |
| A353MVX | | HP | 84 | 95 | Essex County Fire Service | **ex 30 Southend on Sea-1992**<br>D70 Fourth Ave-Harlow<br>WY-Saxon-Simon SS263 |
| A999HAJ | 5 | HP | 84 | | Cleveland County Fire Brigade-**1996**<br>Cleveland Fire Brigade | 9 Stranton West Hartlepool -**ex demonstrator**<br>WY-Carmichael- Bronto 322 |
| A834WGG | | HP | 84 | | Strathclyde Fire Brigade<br>(Scotland) | **ex B07 Parkhead-Glasgow-1992**<br>E01 Bothwell Rd-Hamilton<br>WY-Saxon-Simon SS263 |
| B870AGD | | HP | 85 | | Strathclyde Fire Brigade<br>(Scotland) | **ex A04 North West-Glasgow-1995** / For Re-chassis<br>WY-Angloco-Simon SS263 |
| B871AGD | | HP | 85 | | Strathclyde Fire Brigade<br>(Scotland) | C07 Rue End St-Greenock<br>WY-Angloco-Simon SS263 |
| C831GNO | | HP | 86 | 95 | Essex County Fire Service | **ex A10 Cowdray Ave-Colchester-1993**<br>Reserve-Date<br>WY-Saxon-Simon SS263 |
| D874YFP | | HP | 86 | | Leicestershire Fire Service | SD 30 Lancaster Rd-Leicester -**Refurbished in 1996**<br>WY-Carmichael-Bronto 27.3 |

Photographed on a Fire Brigade Society visit to Lancaster Road fire station in Leicester, D874YFP is a Shelvoke & Drewry WY model that had just returned from the paint shops. Delivered in 1986 from Angloco of Batley, the Bronto Skylift Platform was only the second supplied to a United Kingdom Brigade; the first went to West Hartlepool station of the Cleveland brigade.
*Clive Shearman*

# GERMAN APPLIANCES

| Reg No | Fleet No | TYPE | YR | OS | Appliance & Brigade Name | Details/Stations |
|--------|----------|------|----|----|--------------------------|------------------|
| | | | | | Iveco-Magirus Deutz Chassied Appliances | There were not many UK specials built on the Magirus chassis. Glasgow were the largest user in the late 1960s. Magirus Deutz merged with Iveco (Industrial Vehicles Corporation) the commercial wing of the Italian giant FIAT. From that point on they were badged as Iveco. |
| NGE46F | | Water/E | 67 | 80 | Glasgow Fire Service (Scotland) | B1 South Fire Station-1975-Strathclyde FB 150D-SMT |
| NGE47F | | Water/E | 67 | 80 | Glasgow Fire Service (Scotland) | A1 Ingram St-Central-1975-Strathclyde FB 150D-SMT |
| NYS26F | | TLP | 68 | ? | Glasgow Fire Service (Scotland) | A1 Ingram St-Central-1975-Strathclyde FB Sold to Warwickshire CFB 105D-Bennett-Magirus DLK30 |
| PUS920F | | TLP | 68 | ? | Glasgow Fire Service (Scotland) | C1/A4 Kelbourne St-North West-1975-Strathclyde FB 105D-F&Wylie-Magirus DLK30 |
| PGB276F | | Water/E | 68 | 80 | Glasgow Fire Service (Scotland) | B2 Govan Rd-Govan-1975-Strathclyde FB 150D-SMT |
| PGB277F | | Water/E | 68 | 80 | Glasgow Fire Service (Scotland) | C1/A4 Kelbourne St-North West-1975-Strathclyde FB 150D-SMT |
| VGG291H | | TL | 71 | 82 | Glasgow Fire Service (Scotland) | C4/A7 Kelvinhaugh St-West Marine-1975-Strathclyde FB Tower Ladder fitted with cage 230D-Bennett-Magirus DLK30 |
| Q455GVC | | PM | 80 | 93 | West Glamorgan County Fire Service (Wales) | 8 Sway Rd-Morriston-Swansea -Written off in RTA 170-D16-Lacre PDE |
| A308VEG | | TL | 84 | | Cambridgeshire Fire & Rescue Service | A14 Dogsthorpe Rd-Peterborough Iveco-192 D14-Carmichael-Magirus DLK30E |
| A621SEW | | TL | 84 | | Cambridgeshire Fire & Rescue Service | B01 Parkside-Cambridge Iveco-192 D14-Carmichael-Magirus DLK30E |
| A131KAY | | TL | 84 | | Leicestershire Fire Brigade | SD30 Lancaster Rd-Leicester Central Iveco-256 D14-Carmichael-Magirus DLK23-12 |
| B318VFJ | 5055 | TL | 84 | | Devon Fire Brigade | ex 50-Greenbank-Plymouth-1994 Reserve-Date Iveco-256 D14-Carmichael-Magirus DLK23-12 |
| D950ETC | | TL | 86 | | County of Avon Fire Brigade-1996 Avon Fire Brigade | A1 Temple Back-Central -1996 C5 Hartcliffe Way-Bedminster- Iveco-256 D15-Carmichael-Magirus DLK23-12 |
| D951ETC | | TL | 86 | | County of Avon Fire Brigade-1996 Avon Fire Brigade | B1 Cleveland Bridge-Bath Iveco-256 D15-Carmichael-Magirus DLK23-12 |
| E368LFH | 686 | TL | 88 | | Gloucestershire Fire & Rescue Service | 05 Eastern Ave-Gloucester /Cancelled export order Iveco-140-25 Carmichael-Magirus DLK23-12 |
| FDZ4565 | | TL | 89 | | Northern Ireland Fire Brigade | D07 Northland Rd-Londonderry Iveco-140-25 Carmichael-Magirus DLK30E |
| LDZ7742 | | TL | 92 | | Northern Ireland Fire Brigade | A01 Bankmore St-Belfast Iveco-140-25 Carmichael-Magirus DLK30E |
| L626DOD | 5475 | TL | 94 | | Devon Fire & Rescue Service | ex 50 Greenbank Rd-Greenbank-Plymouth-1996 49 Crownhill Rd-Crownhill-Plymouth Iveco 140-25A-GB Fire-Magirus DLK30E |
| M542MOG | | TL | 95 | | Buckinghamshire Fire & Rescue Service | Sherwood Drive-Bletchley-Milton Keynes Iveco 120-E23-GB Fire-Magirus DLK24PLC |
| M304LBB | 230 | TL | 95 | | Tyne & Wear Metropolitan Fire Brigade | F The Fossway-Walker-Newcastle Iveco 150 E-27/GB Fire-Magirus DLK18-12 |
| N551XKJ | 187 | TL | 96 | | Kent Fire Brigade | 60 Loose Rd-Maidstone Iveco 120-25-GB Fire-Magirus DLK23-12C |

| | | | | | | |
|---|---|---|---|---|---|---|
| P | 188 | TL | 97 | | Kent Fire Brigade | |
| | | | | | | Iveco 120-25-GB Fire-Magirus DLK23-12C |
| P | 189 | TL | 97 | | Kent Fire Brigade | |
| | | | | | | Iveco 120-25-GB Fire-Magirus DLK23-12C |

| | | | | | MAN<br>Chassied Appliances | The M.A.N range goes from the light G90 series through the 12-16 ton D range used in the TL's. The second set of numbers signifies the engine size. |
|---|---|---|---|---|---|---|
| A363JRF | 539 | TL | 83 | | Staffordshire Fire Brigade | SD Moor St-Burton upon Trent<br>16D-240-Angloco-Metz DL30 |
| A210CYJ | | TL | 83 | | East Sussex Fire Brigade | **ex Preston Circus-Brighton-1993**<br>BD22 Beeching Rd-Bexhill<br>16D-240-Angloco-Metz DLK23-12 |
| D900ODW | 76 | TL | 86 | | South Glamorgan Fire & Rescue Service (Wales) | **ex 5 Barry-1988**<br>St Micheals St-Shrewsbury-Shropshire Fire Service<br>12D-192-Angloco-Metz DL30 |
| E184BPN | | TL | 87 | | East Sussex Fire Brigade | BD 11 Whitley Rd-Eastbourne<br>16D-240-Angloco-Metz DL30 |
| G446GHB | | ET | 89 | | South Glamorgan Fire & Rescue -**1996**<br>South Wales Fire Service (Wales) | 04 Crowbridge Rd-Ely-Cardiff<br>G90-F&Wylie |
| G408RAP | | TL | 90 | | East Sussex Fire Brigade | BD 08 Bohemia Rd-Hastings<br>16D-240-Angloco-Metz DL30 |
| J573UDW | | ET | 92 | | South Glamorgan Fire & Rescue-**1996**<br>South Wales Fire Service (Wales) | 03 Heol y Nant-Whitchurch-Cardiff<br>G90-F&Wylie |
| L522NRF | 522 | PMover Foam/C | 93 | | Staffordshire Fire & Rescue Service | Hamil Rd-Burslem-Stoke<br>M17-272-RSG |
| L523NRF | 523 | PMover Foam/C | 93 | | Staffordshire Fire & Rescue Service | Old Hednesford Rd-Cannock<br>M17-272-RSG |
| K693YMO | S15 | CIU | 93 | | Royal Berkshire Fire & Rescue Service | Whitley Wood-Reading<br>11-190-Leicester Carriage Builders |
| L508KAN | S16 | C/Unit | 94 | | Royal Berkshire Fire & Rescue Service | Dee Road-Reading<br>11-190-Leicester Carriage Builders |
| N419RJF | 5500 | PMover BAT | 96 | | Devon Fire & Rescue Service | Headquarters<br>M90-17.232-Penman-Multilift |
| P940YTT | 5535 | PMover BAT | 96 | | Devon Fire & Rescue Service | Headquarters<br>18.244-Penman-Multilift |

| | | | | | Mercedes Benz<br>Chassied Aerial Appliances | Mercedes Benz are the largest producer of heavy trucks in the world. The range goes from 2.5 tons up to 38 tons. |
|---|---|---|---|---|---|---|
| F961RMO | | HP | 89 | | Royal Berkshire Fire & Rescue Service | **ex A01 Caversham Rd-Reading-1992**<br>B20 Whitley Wood-Reading<br>1625-Saxon-Simon SS263 |
| G483LYC | | ALP | 89 | | Somerset Fire Brigade | A01 Lisieux Way-Taunton<br>1625-Saxon-Simon ST240-S |
| G484LYC | | ALP | 89 | | Somerset Fire Brigade | B21 Reckleford-Yeovil<br>1625-Saxon-Simon ST240-S |
| G284CRL | | HP | 90 | 95 | Cornwall County Fire Brigade | 4.1 Station Rd-Truro<br>**Booms off Dodge K1050-RVC273M**<br>**Withdrawn due to problems with the booms.**<br>**Re furbished and used as Simon Access Reserve HP**<br>1625-Saxon-Simon SS220 |
| G35KVG | | HP | 90 | | Norfolk Fire Service | CD 69 Friars Lane-Great Yarmouth<br>1625-Mountain Range-Simon SS263 |
| G459NMW | | ALP | 90 | | Wiltshire Fire Brigade | 3/1 Ashley Rd- Sailsbury<br>2228-Angloco-Bronto 28-2TI |
| J990SOL | S00003 | TL | 91 | | Suffolk Fire Service | **ex A02 Princes St-Ipswich-1993**<br>B01 Fornham Rd-Bury St Edmonds<br>**Ladders re ch off Dodge G16C-Carmichael-C779VGV**<br>1726-Carmichael-Magirus DLK30E |

**Originally serving the town of Barry in South Glamorgan, D900ODW has a MAN 12D-192 chassis with Metz turntable ladder and was sold to the Shropshire Fire Service where is provides support as an aerial appliance based at Shrewsbury. A new Volvo Aerial Ladder Platform is expected to arrive in the county later in 1997. The vehicle differs to those MAN-based Turntable Ladders with Eastbourne and Staffordshire in that this example has a lighter chassis.** *Clive Shearman*

| | | | | | | |
|---|---|---|---|---|---|---|
| J999EST | | ALP | 92 | | Highlands & Islands Fire Brigade (Scotland) | A1 Harbour Rd-Inverness 2624-Angloco-Bronto 28-2TI |
| K639SRT | S00009 | TL | 93 | | Suffolk Fire Service | A02 Princes St-Ipswich-1996 A01 Colchester Rd-Ipswich 1726-Angloco-Metz DLK30 |
| K707LYJ | | TL | 93 | | East Sussex Fire Brigade | A04 Preston Circus-Brighton 1726-Angloco-Metz DLK30 |
| L691XDL | | TL | 94 | | Isle of Wight Fire & Rescue Service | 1 South St-Newport 1726AF-Angloco-Metz DLK30PLC |
| M568DAF | | ALP | 95 | | Cornwall County Fire Brigade | 4.1 Station Rd-Truro 2531-Bedwas-Simon ST290-S |
| M210AOU | | TL | 95 | | County of Avon Fire Brigade -1996 Avon Fire Brigade | C1 Milton Ave-Weston Super Mare 1524-Angloco-Metz DLK30 |
| N601LHT | | TL | 96 | | Avon Fire Brigade | A1 Temple Back-Temple-Bristol 1524-Angloco-Metz DLK30 |
| N926BYC | | HP | 96 | | Somerset Fire Brigade | A02 Salmon Parade-Bridgewater 1824-Saxon-Simon SS263 |
| P137PCV | | ALP | 97 | | Cornwall County Fire Brigade | 5.1 Tregunnel Rd-Newquay 1827-Saxon-Simon ST240-S |
| | | | | | **Mercedes Benz** **Rescue & Emergency Appliances** | |
| D532GVG D481LPW | | Res/T | 87 | | Norfolk Fire Service | C69 Friars Lane-Great Yarmouth/ **Damaged in RTA** 1222F-Polyma FP |
| F835OHW | | Res/T | 89 | | County of Avon Fire Brigade-1996 Avon Fire Brigade | B1 Cleveland Bridge-Bath 917AF-F&Wylie |
| F271DNT | 70 | ET | 89 | | Shropshire Fire Service | **ex A Div St Michael's St-Shrewsbury-1995**/Reserve-917AF-Saxon |
| F854DWA | | Heavy Res/T | 89 | | South Yorkshire County Fire Service | E18 Fitzwilliam St-Rotherham 917AF-Carmichael |
| F680MTS | | Res/U | 89 | | Tayside Fire Brigade (Scotland) | B7 Atholl Rd-Pitlochry 609D-Tayside FB |
| F681MTS | | Res/U | 89 | | Tayside Fire Brigade (Scotland) | B8 High St-Kinross 609D-Tayside FB |
| G958BRU | | Res/T | 89 | | West Glamorgan County FS-1996 Mid & West Wales FB (Wales) | 8/S8 Sway Rd-Morriston-Swansea 917AF-HCB Angus |
| G486LYC | | Res/T | 89 | | Somerset Fire Brigade | B21 Reckleford-Yeovil 711D-Saxon |
| G431MTS | | Res/U | 89 | | Tayside Fire Brigade (Scotland) | A5 Garrison Rd-Montrose 609D-Tayside FB |
| G432MTS | | Res/U | 89 | | Tayside Fire Brigade (Scotland) | A7 Academy St-Forfar 609D-Tayside FB |
| G464NMW | | Res/T | 90 | | Wiltshire Fire Brigade | 3/1 Ashley Rd-Sailsbury 917AF-Mountain Range |
| G470NMW | | Res/T | 90 | | Wiltshire Fire Brigade | 2/1 Dallas Rd-Chippenham 920AF-Rosenbaur |
| G471NMW | | Res/T | 90 | | Wiltshire Fire Brigade | 1/7 The Chesters-Westlea-Swindon 917AF-Mountain Range |
| G265VBP | A00008 | Crash Res/T | 90 | | West Sussex Fire Brigade | 09/B08 Ilfield Ave-Crawley -**Fitted Foam Supply** 917AF-Mountain Range |
| G726WBH | W082 | Res/T | 90 | | Hertfordshire County Fire & Rescue Service | B18 Wellfield Rd-Hatfield 917AF-HCB Angus |
| H949EDE | | ET | 90 | | Dyfed Fire Brigade-1996 Mid & West Wales FB (Wales) | B1/W11 Merlins Hill-Haverfordwest -**HIAB 071** crane fitted 1120AF-Carmichael |
| H950EDE | | MRU | 90 | | Dyfed Fire Brigade-1996 Mid & West Wales FB (Wales) | B2/W12 Yorke St-Milford Haven **Tows In-shore rescue boat-5.4 Avon Mariner** 609D-Hoskins |
| H616EEJ | | ET | 90 | | Dyfed Fire Brigade-1996 Mid & West Wales FB (Wales) | C1/N2 Trefechan-Aberystwyth-**HIAB 071** crane fitted 1120AF-Carmichael |

| | | | | | | |
|---|---|---|---|---|---|---|
| **H478OWO** | | Res/T | 91 | | Mid Glamorgan County FS-**1996**<br>South Wales Fire Service (Wales) | 21 Dynevor St-Merthyr Tydfil<br>1120AF-HCB Angus |
| **H481OWO** | | Res/T | 91 | | Mid Glamorgan County FS-**1996**<br>South Wales Fire Service (Wales) | 01 Angel St-Bridgend<br>1120AF-HCB Angus |
| **H483OWO** | | Res/T | 91 | | Mid Glamorgan County FS-**1996**<br>South Wales Fire Service(Wales) | 15 Oxford St-Pontypridd<br>1120AF-HCB Angus |
| **H623EBX** | | ET | 91 | | Dyfed Fire Brigade-**1996**<br>Mid & West Wales FB (Wales) | A1/W1 Corporation Ave-Llanelli -**HIAB 071** crane fitted<br>1120AF-Carmichael |
| **H351VVV** | | Heavy<br>Res/T | 91 | | Northamptonshire Fire & Rescue<br>Service | S10 Mereway-Northampton-**HIAB 140** crane fitted<br>1625-Rosenbaur |
| **H410CEW** | | Res/T | 91 | | Cambridgeshire Fire & Rescue Service | A14 Dogsthorpe Rd-Peterborough<br>811D-Carmichael |
| **H734LEY** | | ET | 91 | | Gwynedd Fire Service -**1996**<br>North Wales Fire Service (Wales) | 16/W04 Arran Rd-Dolgellau<br>811D-Carmichael |
| **H151JFL** | | Res/T | 91 | | Cambridgeshire Fire & Rescue Service | A27 Hartford Rd-Huntingdon<br>1120AF-Rosenbaur |
| **H681EDL** | | Res/T | 91 | | Isle of Wight Fire & Rescue Service | 01 South St-Newport<br>917AF-Sparshatts |

**Photographed at Bridgewater fire station in Somerset, N826BYC is based on a Mercedes-Benz 1824 chassis and features a Hydraulic Platform and Saxon bodywork. This appliance is unusual in that it was the first Mercedes-Benz since 1990 fitted with Simon SS263 booms, all subsequent aerials have ladder platform configurations.** *Clive Shearman*

| | | | | | | |
|---|---|---|---|---|---|---|
| H517CGD | | RRU | 91 | | Strathclyde Fire Brigade (Scotland) | B05 Calder Rd-Polmadie-Glasgow 410D-F&Wylie |
| H669OLS | | ESU | 91 | | Central Region Fire Brigade-**1996** Central Scotland FB (Scotland) | S8 Ranoch Rd-Stirling-**HIAB 071** crane fitted 917AF-Mountain Range |
| J603HGB | | RRU | 92 | | Strathclyde Fire Brigade (Scotland) | A05 Anniesland Rd-Knightswood-Glasgow 410D-Emergency One |
| J827CVF | | Res/T | 92 | | Norfolk Fire Service | A27 Bethel St-Norwich 1222F-Halton FP |
| J830CVF | | Res/T | 92 | | Norfolk Fire Service | B47 Kilhams Lane-Kings Lynn 1222F-Halton FP |
| K805GYD | | Res/T | 92 | | Somerset Fire Brigade | A01 Lisieux Way-Taunton 814D-Saxon |
| K591SJX | | SIU | 92 | | West Yorkshire Fire Service | CD South Lane-Elland -**Fitted HIAB 071 Crane** Unimog 2150L-WYFS |
| K938UDG | 712 | Res/T | 93 | | Gloucestershire Fire & Rescue Service | 12 Keynsham Rd-Cheltenham-**Fitted with HIAB 071 Crane** 1120AF-Locomotors |
| K753LWS | | Res/T | 93 | | County of Avon Fire Brigade-**1996** Avon Fire Brigade | C1 Milton St-Weston super Mare 917AF-F&Wylie-Saxon |
| K658MBP | A00078 | Res/T | 93 | | West Sussex Fire Brigade | 17 Northgate-Chichester-**Fitted HIAB 071 crane** 1124AF-John Dennis CB |
| K659MBP | A00079 | Res/T | 93 | | West Sussex Fire Brigade | 01 Ardsheal Rd-Worthing-**Fitted HIAB 071 crane** 1124AF-John Dennis CB |
| K644DJB | | RSV | 93 | | Royal Berkshire Fire & Rescue Service | 04 Hawthorne Rd-Newbury-**Fitted Palfinger 7000 crane** 1120AF-Locomotors |
| K499PFT | U26 | OSU | 93 | | Northumberland Fire & Rescue Service | CD Tyne Mill-Hexham 310D-Zeta |
| L806USU | | RRU | 94 | | Strathclyde Fire Brigade (Scotland) | D01 Station Rd-Ayr 410D-Emergency One |
| L351PFL | | Res/T DCU | 94 | | Cambridgeshire Fire & Rescue Service | B01 Parkside-Cambridge 1124AF-Angloco |
| L25TMW | | Res/T | 94 | | Wiltshire Fire Brigade | 4/1 Hilperton Rd-Trowbridge 1124AF-Devcoplan |
| L155XGE | | RRU | 95 | | Strathclyde Fire Brigade (Scotland) | C05 Paisley Rd-Renfrew 418D-Emergency One |
| M53BEY | | ET | 95 | | County of Clwyd Fire Brigade-**1996** North Wales Fire Service (Wales) | E1/E02 Bradley Rd-Wrexham-**Fitted HIAB 090 Crane** 1124AF-Angloco-**Saxon (cab)** |
| N23DJC | | ET | 96 | | County of Clwyd Fire Brigade-**1996** North Wales Fire Service (Wales) | W2/C02 Abergale Rd-Colwyn Bay 1124-Angloco |
| N298NGG | | RRU | 96 | | Strathclyde Fire Brigade (Scotland) | F07 Castlegreen St-Dumbarton 412D-Emergency One |
| N704VFO | | Res/T | 96 | | Mid & West Wales Fire Brigade (Wales) | Llandiloes Rd-Newtown-**Ordered by Powys Fire Service** 817D-Excalibur |
| N705VFO | | Res/T | 96 | | Mid & West Wales Fire Brigade (Wales) | Camden Rd-Brecon -**Ordered by Powys Fire Service** 817D-Excalibur |
| | A000 | Heavy Res/T | 96 | | West Sussex Fire Brigade | 1124AF-John Dennis CB |
| P136PCV | | Res/T | 96 | | Cornwall County Fire Brigade | 7.1 Berrycombe Rd-Bodmin 1124AF-Carmichael International |
| P138PCV | | Res/T | 96 | | Cornwall County Fire Brigade | 2.1 College St-Cambourne 1124AF-Carmichael International |

| | | | | | Mercedes Benz Specialist Appliances | |
|---|---|---|---|---|---|---|
| D655HHV | S00007 | WRC | 87 | | Suffolk Fire Service | 05 Saxmundaham Rd-Framlingham 1726-Dairy Crest |
| E802EPM | | CAV | 88 | | Surrey Fire & Rescue Service | WD 27 Binham Meadow-Dunsfold 609D-SF&RS |
| F518HRC | S00008 | WRC | 89 | | Suffolk Fire Service | 25 St Georges St-Sudbury 1726-Dairy Crest |
| F898KYS | | TSU | 89 | | Strathclyde Fire Brigade (Scotland) | B02 Govan Rd-Govan-Glasgow 814D-Scott-SFB |
| G485LYC | | WRC | 89 | | Somerset Fire Brigade | A02 Salmon Parade-Bridgewater 1622-Saxon |
| G538STS | | PMover BA Trg | 90 | | Tayside Fire Brigade (Scotland) | A1 Blackness Rd-Dundee 1114-Powell Duffryn-Rolonoff-Penman |
| G539STS | | PM /OSU BAU | 90 | | Tayside Fire Brigade (Scotland) | A3 North Balmossie St-Monfeith 1114-Powell Duffryn-Rolonoff-Penman |
| H515CGD | | FoT Salv/T | 91 | | Strathclyde Fire Brigade (Scotland) | F1 Kilbowie Rd-Clydebank 811D-F&Wylie |
| H516CGD | | FoT Salv/T | 91 | | Strathclyde Fire Brigade (Scotland) | D5 Coreshill Mount Rd-Dreghorn 811D-F&Wylie |
| | | | | | | **The London Fire Brigade never actually put the Light Rescue Unit appliances on the run. I saw one at G38 Heston partially kitted with light rescue kit and paramedic items but the idea never took hold.** |
| H861XYF | CSU-1 | CSU | 91 | 96 | London Fire Brigade | **ex LRU-A39 Finchley** Training/Reserve(**Written off in RTA**) 917AF-Locomotors |
| H862XYF | CSU-2 | CSU | 91 | | London Fire Brigade | **ex LRU-G38 Heston/** G30 Harrow Rd-Wembley (**WC**) 917AF-Locomotors |
| H863XYF | CSU-3 | CSU | 91 | | London Fire Brigade | **ex LRU-E21 Lewisham/** E20 High St-Lewisham (**SC**) 917AF-Locomotors |
| H864XYF | CSU-4 | CSU | 91 | | London Fire Brigade | **ex LRU-H31 Croydon** / H30 Old Town-Croydon 917AF-Locomotors |
| H865XYF | CSU-5 | CSU | 91 | | London Fire Brigade | **ex LRU-F44 East Ham/** F20 Romford Rd-Stratford (**EC**) 917AF-Locomotors |
| H866XYF | CSU-6 | CSU | 91 | | London Fire Brigade | **ex LRU-A23 Euston/ A20 Paddington-1995/** West Reserve- 917AF-Locomotors |
| H521YAP | | FOT | 91 | | East Sussex Fire Brigade | A06 Fort Rd-Newhaven 917AF-Boughton-ESFB |
| J58BYB | | WRC | 91 | | Somerset Fire Brigade | B21 Reckleford-Yeovil 1722-Saxon |
| J61BYB | | C/Unit | 91 | | Somerset Fire Brigade | A02 Salmon Parade-Bridgewater 814D-Saxon |
| J960CRB | W086 | C/Unit | 91 | | Hertfordshire Fire & Rescue Service | B18 Wellfield Rd-Hatfield 814D-Leicester Carriage Builders |
| K45AVV | | HLL | 93 | | Northamptonshire Fire & Rescue Service | SD 9 Moulton Way-Moulton 1726-Bence |
| K69YBO | | C/Unit | 93 | | Gwent Fire Brigade-**1996** South Wales Fire Service (Wales) | B20/32 Henllys Way-Cwmbran 814D-Optare-Saxon |
| K311OCR | | WRC FOC | 93 | | Surrey Fire & Rescue Service | ED 14 Eastbourne Rd-Godstone F1726-Maidment Tankers |
| K312OCR | | WRC FOC | 93 | | Surrey Fire & Rescue Service | ED 12 Spook Hill-Dorking F1726-Maidment Tankers |
| K313OCR | | WRC FOC | 93 | | Surrey Fire & Rescue Service | ED 13 Cobham Rd-Leatherhead F1726-Maidment Tankers |
| K314OCR | | WRC FOC | 93 | | Surrey Fire & Rescue Service | WD 26 Guilford Rd-Farnham F1726-Maidment Tankers |

This attractive Mercedes-Benz 814D Control Unit was delivered in 1993 to Cwmbran in Gwent.  It was bodied by Optare, a well known bus-body builder, to its Star-Rider design and equipped for fire brigade duties by Saxon.  Since 1996, Cwmbran has become part of the newly formed South Wales Fire Service. *Clive Shearman*

| K315OCR | | WRC FOC | 93 | | Surrey Fire & Rescue Service | ND 37 London Rd-Camberley F1726-Maidment Tankers |
|---|---|---|---|---|---|---|
| K89SCC | | C/Unit | 93 | | Gwynedd Fire Service-**1996** North Wales Fire Service (Wales) | 09W01 Llanberis Rd-Caernarfon 609D-Saxon |
| L691GPY | | ISU | 94 | | North Yorkshire Fire & Rescue Service | S2 Boroughbridge Rd-Acomb-York 817D-Bott-North Yorkshire F&RS |
| L452TFL | | OSU | 94 | | Cambridgeshire Fire & Rescue Service | A27 Hartford Rd-Huntingdon 814D-Gladwins |
| L140VCE | | WRC | 94 | | Cambridgeshire Fire & Rescue Service | A27 Hartford Rd-Huntingdon 2531-Carmichael International |
| L944UAF | | C/Unit | 94 | | Cornwall County Fire Brigade | 4.1 Station Rd-Truro 814D-Cornwall County FB |
| L345LET | | OSU | 94 | | South Yorkshire County Fire Service | 26 Tankersley Fire Station 2527-Curtainsider-Moffat-Swain & Bradshaw |
| L704MKY | | PM /DCU Salv/T | 94 | | South Yorkshire County Fire Service | **20 Knolbeck Lane-Brampton Bierlow-1995** 26 Tankersley- 1820-Lacre-Williams |
| L705MKY | | PMover WRC | 94 | | South Yorkshire County Fire Service | **20 Knolbeck Lane-Brampton Bierlow-1995** 26 Tankersley- 1820-Lacre-Williams |
| M344HDL | | Support Unit | 95 | | Isle of Wight Fire & Rescue Service | 01 South St-Newport 609D-IWF&RS |
| N284HEX | | CIU | 95 | | Norfolk Fire Brigade | 29 Chartwell Rd-Sprowston-Norwich 814D-Saxon |
| N477PDL | | Incident Control/U | 96 | | Isle of Wight Fire & Rescue Service | 01 South St-Newport 814D-Saxon |
| P95JYC | | FS/Unit | 97 | | Somerset Fire Brigade | 817D-Saxon |
| P96JYC | | FS/Unit | 97 | | Somerset Fire Brigade | 817D-Saxon |

Rescue Tender M974JWO was delivered to Malpas station in Newport, Gwent in 1995. It is one of a pair, the other being stationed at Ebbw Vale in the northern area of the new South Wales Fire Service. M974JWO has a 4x4 wheel drive configuration that suits the terrain in which it serves. *Clive Shearman*

# SCANDINAVIAN

| Reg No | Fleet No | TYPE | YR | OS | Appliance & Brigade Name | Details/Stations |
|--------|----------|------|----|----|--------------------------|------------------|
| | | | | | **Scania Chassied** **Aerial Appliances** | |
| SSO66X | | TL | 81 | 93 | Grampian Fire Brigade (Scotland) | SD96 King St-Aberdeen Ladder re-chassied onto K286FSO LB81-Angloco-Metz DLK30 |
| A995DSS | | TL | 84 | 94 | Grampian Fire Brigade (Scotland) | SD 97 Souterhead Rd-Altens-Aberdeen -1996 SD 96 King St-Aberdeen **Severely damaged in RTA** G92M-Angloco-Metz Metz DLK30 |
| C812JGB | | TL | 86 | | Strathclyde Fire Brigade (Scotland) | D02 Campbell St-Kilmarnock G92M-Angloco-Metz DLK30 |
| D549RGG | | TL | 87 | | Strathclyde Fire Brigade (Scotland) | C04 Canal St-Paisley G92M-Angloco-Metz DLK30 |
| D995PKN | 191 | ALP | 87 | | Kent Fire Brigade | S60 Loose Rd-Maidstone-1996 43 Watling St-Rochester-Medway G92M-Carmichael-Bronto 28-2TI |
| E717SON | | ALP | 87 | | Cheshire Fire Brigade | **ex Bronto Skylift demonstrator** A1 St Anne's St Chester G92M-Carmichael-Bronto 28-2TI |
| E604LHN | 35 | HP | 87 | | Cleveland County Fire Brigade-**1996** Cleveland Fire Brigade | 1 Park Rd South-Middlesborough P92M-Saxon-Simon SS263 |
| E812ASA | | HP | 87 | | Grampian Fire Brigade (Scotland) | ED 77 North Anderson Drive-Aberdeen P93M-Saxon-Simon SS263 |
| E689SEA | 246 | HP | 87 | | Tayside Fire Brigade (Scotland) | BD 1 High St-Perth P92M-F&Wylie-Simon SS263 |
| E704WGB | | TL | 87 | | Strathclyde Fire Brigade (Scotland) | F01 Kilbowie Rd-Clydebank G92M-Angloco-Metz DLK30 |
| E991WNS | | TL | 87 | | Strathclyde Fire Brigade (Scotland) | B05 Calder St-Polmadie-Glasgow G92M-Angloco-Metz DLK30 |
| E750MDE | | TL | 87 | | Dyfed Fire Brigade-**1996** Mid & West Wales FB-(Wales) | B1/W11 Merlin's Hill-Haverfordwest G92M-Angloco-Metz DL30 |
| E497WKO | 192 | ALP | 88 | | Kent Fire Brigade | N35 Coldharbour Rd-Thameside G92M-Carmichael-Bronto 28-2TI |
| E498WKO | 186 | TL | 88 | | Kent Fire Brigade | **ex Margate Rd-Thanet-1992** ND 80 Upper Bridge St-Canterbury P93M-Carmichael-Magirus DL30E |
| E499WKO | 193 | ALP | 88 | | Kent Fire Brigade | S74 Grove Hill Rd-Tunbridge Wells G92M-Carmichael-Bronto 28-2TI |
| E695YNS | | HP | 88 | | Strathclyde Fire Brigade (Scotland) | E04 Main St-Coatbridge G92M-Saxon-Simon SS263 |
| E753JDL | | ALP | 88 | | Isle of Wight Fire & Rescue Service | 01 South St-Newport G92M-Angloco-Bronto 22-2TI |
| F204FHS | | TL | 88 | | Strathclyde Fire Brigade (Scotland) | B07 Cuthelton St-Parkhead-Glasgow G93M-Angloco-Metz DLK30 |
| F62RTC | F/60/89 | ALP | 89 | | County of Avon Fire Brigade-**1996** Avon Fire Brigade | A3 St Andrews Rd-Avonmouth G93M-Carmichael-Bronto 22-2TI |
| G272UNK | 7 | ALP | 90 | | Bedfordshire Fire & Rescue Service | 00 Studley Rd-Luton / **Damaged in serious RTA** G93M-Angloco-Bronto 28-2TI |
| G216YTW | | HP | 90 | | West Glamorgan County FS-**1996** Mid & West Wales FB (Wales) | 8/S8 Sway Rd-Morriston-Swansea P93M-Bedwas-Simon SS220 |
| G646ABX | | TL | 90 | | Dyfed Fire Brigade-**1996** Mid & West Wales FB (Wales) | A2/W2 Lime Grove Avenue-Carmarthen G93M-Angloco-Metz DLK30 |

| | | | | | | |
|---|---|---|---|---|---|---|
| G429KBO | | TL | 90 | | West Glamorgan County FS-**1996** Mid & West Wales FB (Wales) | 8/S8 Sway Rd-Morriston-Swansea **Ladders off Dodge G16C-C310JEP** G93M-Angloco-Metz DLK30 |
| G434KBO | | ALP | 90 | | Mid Glamorgan Fire Brigade-**1996** South Wales Fire Service (Wales) | 15 Oxford St-Pontypridd/**Originally single rear axle** G93M-Saxon-Simon ST240-S |
| H299HSW | | ALP | 90 | | Dumfries & Galloway Fire Brigade (Scotland) | AD Brooms Rd-Dumfries G93M-Angloco-Bronto 28-2TI |
| DDC1 | 23 | ALP | 91 | | Cleveland County Fire Brigade-**1996** Cleveland Fire Brigade | 2 South Rd-Norton-Stockton P93M-Saxon-Simon STS300-S |
| H105YBD | | ALP | 91 | | Northamptonshire Fire & Rescue Service | SD The Mounts-Northampton G93M-Angloco-Bronto 28-2TI |
| H277HVX | | ALP | 91 | | Essex County Fire & Rescue Service | B34/E34 Rainsford Lane-Chelmsford P113H-Saxon-Simon ST300-S |
| J754AAR | | ALP | 92 | | Essex County Fire & Rescue Service | B30/E30 Sutton Rd-Southend on Sea P113H-Saxon-Simon ST300-S |
| J114UPU | | ALP | 92 | | Essex County Fire & Rescue Service | **ex C52 Basildon-1994** A10/E10 Cowdray Ave-Colchester P113H-Saxon-Simon ST300-S |
| J21PJC | | ALP | 92 | | County of Clwyd Fire Brigade-**1996** North Wales Fire Service (Wales) | E1/E01 Bradley Rd-Wrexham P113M-Angloco-Bronto 28-2TI |
| K377MYS | | ALP | 93 | | Strathclyde Fire Brigade (Scotland) | **ex A1 Port Dundas Rd-Cowcaddens-1996** A7 Kelvinhaugh St-Yorkhill (**formerly A7 'West'**) P113M-Angloco-Bronto F30 HDT |
| K286FSO | | TL | 93 | | Grampian Fire Brigade (Scotland) | **ex SD 96 King St-Aberdeen-1996** N71 Ugie St-Peterhead **Ladders off Scania LB81-SSO66X** P93M-Angloco-Metz DLK30 |
| K667BPY | | TL | 93 | | North Yorkshire Fire & Rescue Service | SD 1 Clifford St-York P93M-Bedwas-Camiva EPA 30 |
| K629OAM | | Pump HP | 93 | | Wiltshire Fire Brigade | 1/1 Drove Rd-Swindon P93ML-Saxon-Italmac 28m |
| L547FTM | 14 | ALP | 93 | | Bedfordshire Fire & Rescue Service | 01 Barkers Lane-Bedford P93M-Angloco-Bronto 28-2TI |
| L46JVV | | TL | 93 | | Northamptonshire Fire & Rescue Service | ND 11 Headlands-Kettering G93M-Angloco-Metz DLK30 |
| L29DDW | | HP | 93 | | Gwent Fire Brigade-**1996** South Wales Fire Service (Wales) | B11/46 Archibald St-Maindee-Newport P93M-Saxon-Simon SS263 |
| L663LOO | | ALP | 94 | | Essex County Fire & Rescue Service | C52/W52 Broadmayne-Basildon P113H-Saxon-Simon ST290-S |
| M473SSX | | ALP | 94 | | Lothian & Borders Fire Brigade (Scotland) | 31 Calder Rd-Sighthill Damaged in serious RTA/Repaired P113H-Bedwas-Simon ST290-S |
| M543SRF | 543 | ALP | 94 | | Staffordshire Fire & Rescue Service | Lammascote Rd-Stafford P113H-Angloco-Bronto F30 HDT |
| M58FYS | | ALP | 95 | | Strathclyde Fire Brigade (Scotland) | A1 Port Dundas Rd-Cowcaddens-Glasgow P113H-Angloco-Bronto F32HDT |
| N503GJN | | ALP | 96 | | Essex County Fire & Rescue Service | W70 Fourth Ave-Harlow P113H-Saxon-Simon ALP340 |

| | | | | | | |
|---|---|---|---|---|---|---|
| | | | | | **Scania Chassied** **Specialist Appliances** | |
| F793AWO | | PMover | 89 | | West Glamorgan County FS-**1996** Mid & West Wales FB (Wales) | 8/S8 Sway Rd-Morriston-Swansea G93M-Lacre PDE |
| F998HDS | | WRC | 89 | | Strathclyde Fire Brigade (Scotland) | Training School-Cheapside G93M-F&Wylie |
| F999HDS | | WRC | 89 | | Strathclyde Fire Brigade (Scotland) | Training School-Cheapside G93M-F&Wylie |
| F428TDE | | FOT | 89 | | Dyfed Fire Brigade-**1996** Mid & West Wales FB (Wales) | B2/W12 Yorke St-Milford Haven G93M-Angloco |

| | | | | | | | |
|---|---|---|---|---|---|---|---|
| F429TDE | | | PM/HazM FOC/CAV | 89 | | Dyfed Fire Brigade-**1996** Mid & West Wales FB (Wales) | B6/W16 High St-Pembroke Dock G93M-Rolonoff-Hoskins-Fergussons |
| G495SYS | | | Heavy Res/T | 90 | | Strathclyde Fire Brigade (Scotland) | A2 Grudie Rd-Easterhouse G93M-Dependable-SFB |
| G522VWS | F/64/90 | | MRT | 90 | | County of Avon Fire Brigade-**1996** Avon Fire Brigade | A5 Rodway Rd-Patchway **Fitted HIAB 071 crane** P113M-Wreckers International |
| H549MDW | | | PMover | 90 | | West Glamorgan County FS-**1996** Mid & West Wales FB (Wales) | 8/S8 Sway Rd-Morriston-Swansea G93M-Lacre PDE-Rolonof |
| H291SSA | | | PMover FOC/BAT CIU | 90 | | Grampian Fire Brigade (Scotland) | E77 North Anderson Drive-Aberdeen S97 Souterhead Rd-Altens-Aberdeen G93M-Multilift-Powell Duffryn |
| J930MBX | | | Heavy Rec/V | 92 | | Dyfed Fire Brigade-**1996** Mid & West Wales FB (Wales) | A2/W2 Lime Grove-Carmarthen G93M-Interstater |
| K428YDW | | | PMover | 92 | | West Glamorgan County FS-**1996** Mid & West Wales FB (Wales) | 8/S8 Sway Rd-Morriston-Swansea **Morriston houses all the pods for WGFB** **G93M-Lacre PDE** |
| K385DOO | | | C/Unit | 93 | | Essex County Fire & Rescue Service | Headquarters G93M-Leicester Carriage Builders |
| L47JVV | | | WRC Foam/C | 93 | | Northamptonshire Fire & Rescue Service | SD4 Staverton Rd-Daventry G93M-Mandate Tankers Ltd |
| L26DDW | | | CIU | 93 | | Gwent Fire Brigade-**1996** South Wales Fire Service (Wales) | B20/32 Henlly's Way-Cwmbran P93M-Angloco |
| L675LOO | | | MRT | 94 | | Essex County Fire & Rescue Service | W50 Hogg Lane-Gray's G93M-Leicester Carriage Builders/Moffat Mounty |
| L676LOO | | | MRT | 94 | | Essex County Fire & Rescue Service | E10 Cowdray Ave-Colchester G93M-Leicester Carriage Builders/Moffat Mounty |
| L677LOO | | | MRT | 94 | | Essex County Fire & Rescue Service | E31 Mountdale Gardens-Leigh on Sea G93M-Leicester Carriage Builders/Moffat Mounty |
| L726UGA | | | C/Unit | 94 | | Strathclyde Fire Brigade (Scotland) | C1 Kings Rd-Johnstone N113.DRB-Leicester Carriage Builders |
| M539UNO | | | Foam/C | 94 | | Essex County Fire & Rescue Service | C50 Hogg Lane-Grays G93H-Leicester Carriage Builders/Moffat Mounty |
| M973JWO | | | Res/T | 94 | | Gwent Fire Brigade-**1996** South Wales Fire Service (Wales) | C05/37 Cemetery Rd-Ebbw Vale P93H-Saxon |
| M974JWO | | | Res/T | 94 | | Gwent Fire Brigade-**1996** South Wales Fire Service (Wales) | B09/45 Malpas Rd-Malpas-Newport P93H-Saxon |
| M472SSX | | | HR/Unit | 94 | | Lothian & Borders Fire Brigade (Scotland) | 36 Newcraighill-Edingburgh G93M-Emergency One |
| N402XRS | | | PMover H/Rescue | 96 | | Grampian Fire Brigade (Scotland) | E77 North Anderson Drive-Aberdeen P93H-Multi-Lift-Powell Duffryn-Emergency One-**Hiab 071** |
| N403XRS | | | PMover | 96 | | Grampian Fire Brigade (Scotland) | E71 Ugie St-Peterhead P93H-Multi-Lift-Powell Duffryn-Emergency One |
| P867LSC | | | IS/Unit | 96 | | Lothian & Borders Fire Brigade (Scotland) | G93M-Penman |

| | | | | | Volvo Chassied Aerial Appliances | |
|---|---|---|---|---|---|---|
| D240ELJ | | TL | 86 | | Dorset Fire Brigade | **ex B18 Wimborne Rd-Poole -1995**<br>**Reserve**-B23 Alm Hurst Rd-Westbourne<br>FL6-16-Angloco-Metz DL30 |
| D429EHN | | TL | 86 | | North Yorkshire Fire Brigade | ED 1 North Marine Drive-Scarborough<br>FL6-17-Angloco-Metz DL30 |
| E280NVN | | TL | 87 | | North Yorkshire Fire Brigade | WD 1 Skipton Rd-Harrogate<br>**Ladders Re-ch off-ERF 84PS-OYT509R-London FB**<br>FL6-1-Carmichael-Magirus DL30H |
| E50MEL | | HP | 87 | | Dorset Fire Brigade | B23 Almhurst Rd-Westbourne<br>**Booms re chassied off Dennis RLJ999X**<br>FL6-16-HCB Angus Simon SS263 |
| E998AHH | 03-01 | TL | 88 | | Cumbria Fire Service | CD Warwick St-Carlisle<br>FL6-17-Carmichael-Magirus DL30E |
| E999AHH | 03-02 | TL | 88 | | Cumbria Fire Service | BD Abbey Rd-Barrow in Furrness<br>FL6-17-Carmichael-Magirus DL30E |
| MAN999U | | TL | 88 | | Isle of Man Fire & Rescue Service | 1 Peel Rd-Douglas<br>FL6-17-AnglocoMetz DL30M |
| E159DVH | 009 | TL | 88 | | West Yorkshire Fire Service | DD Brunswick St-Wakefield<br>FL6-17-Angloco-Metz DL30 |
| F847SHD | 003 | HP | 88 | | West Yorkshire Fire Service | AD Kirkstall Rd-Leeds<br>FL6-17-Saxon-Simon SS263 |
| F848SHD | | FOT Simoniter | 88 | 95 | West Yorkshire Fire Service | AD Corporation St-Morley-Leeds<br>**Boom re chassied off Ford-KTD615K**<br>FL6-14-WYFS-Simon TSM15 |
| F868SHD | 010 | TL | 88 | | West Yorkshire Fire Service | DD Carlinghow Lane-Batley<br>FL6-17-Angloco-Metz DL30 |
| F986NRV | | TL | 88 | | Hampshire Fire & Rescue Service | B24 Somers Rd-Southsea-Portsmouth<br>FL6-17-Angloco-Metz DL30 |
| F922YCM | 1246 | TL | 89 | | Merseyside Fire Brigade | N7 Manchester Rd-Southport<br>**Ladders Re-ch off ERF 84PS-GYM268N-London FB**<br>FL6-17-Angloco-Metz DL30 |
| F999AWU | | ALP | 89 | | South Yorkshire County Fire Service | W23 Darnall Rd-Sheffield-**Booms written of in Accident**<br>FL10-Saxon-Simon ST300-S-**Now HGV lorry** |
| G761LKH | | TL | 89 | | Humberside Fire Brigade | B3 Bessingby Rd-Bridlington<br>FL6-17-Angloco-Metz DL30 |
| GDZ5375 | | HP | 89 | | Northern Ireland Fire Brigade | A06 Upper Newtownards Knock-Belfast<br>FL6-17-Saxon-Simon SS263 |
| G790OAO | 03-03 | TL | 90 | | Cumbria Fire Service | AD King St-Workington<br>FL6-17-Carmichael-Magirus DL30E |
| G220FFX | | ALP | 90 | | Dorset Fire Brigade | A07 North Quay-Weymouth<br>FL6-17-Saxon-Simon ST240-S |
| G775UBW | | ALP | 90 | | Oxfordshire Fire & Rescue Service | B01 Rewley Rd-Oxford<br>FL10-Angloco-Bronto 28-2TI |
| H126OKG | | ALP | 90 | | South Glamorgan Fire & Rescue-1996<br>South Wales Fire Service (Wales) | 01 Adam St-Cardiff-**Seriously damaged in accident**<br>FL10-Saxon-Simon ST300-S |
| H188AFJ | 5359 | ALP | 90 | | Devon Fire & Rescue Service | 48 Ferndale Rd-Camels Head-Plymouth<br>FL10-Angloco-Bronto 28-2TI |
| H901XYF | ALP-1 | ALP | 90 | | London Fire Brigade | A28 Upper Thames St-Dowgate<br>FL10-Angloco-Bronto 33-2TI |
| H902XYF | ALP-2 | ALP | 90 | | London Fire Brigade | A33 49 St Loys Rd-Tottenham<br>FL10-Angloco-Bronto 33-2TI |
| H903XYF | ALP-3 | ALP | 90 | | London Fire Brigade | H34 Kingston Rd-Wimbledon<br>FL10-Angloco-Bronto 33-2TI |
| H904XYF | ALP-4 | ALP | 90 | | London Fire Brigade | G30 591 Harrow Rd-Wembley<br>FL10-Angloco-Bronto 33-2TI |

| | | | | | | |
|---|---|---|---|---|---|---|
| H905XYF | ALP-5 | ALP | 90 | | London Fire Brigade | E31 Stanstead Rd-Forest Hill<br>FL10-Angloco-Bronto 33-2TI |
| H906XYF | ALP-6 | ALP | 90 | | London Fire Brigade | F45 Prince Regent Lane-Plaistow<br>FL10-Angloco-Bronto 33-2TI |
| H179UCX | 011 | TL | 90 | | West Yorkshire Fire Service | BD Bradford Rd-Keighley<br>FL6-17-Angloco-Metz DL30 |
| H180UCX | 012 | TL | 90 | | West Yorkshire Fire Service | BD Thornton Rd-Fairweather Green-Bradford<br>FL6-17-Angloco-Metz DL30 |
| H204MOK | 120 | ALP | 91 | | West Midlands Fire Service | **ex B3-Coventry-1993**/ C4-Bristol Rd-Bournbrook<br>**Taken to Simon Access to have Booms changed to ST290-S**  FL10-Saxon-Simon ST300-S |
| H299XRR | | ALP | 91 | | Nottinghamshire Fire & Rescue Service | 01 Rosemary St-Mansfield<br>FL10-Saxon-Simon ST240-S |
| H157GBG | 1277 | CPL | 91 | | Merseyside Fire Brigade | N3 Storrington Ave-Liverpool<br>FL10-Angloco-Bronto 28-2TI |
| H158GBG | 1278 | CPL | 91 | | Merseyside Fire Brigade | C3 Canning Place-Wapping-Liverpool<br>FL10-Angloco-Bronto 28-2TI |
| J869MFJ | 5383 | ALP | 92 | | Devon Fire & Rescue Service | 32 Howells Rd-Exeter<br>FL10-Angloco-Bronto 28-2TI |
| J688MTA | 5400 | ALP | 92 | | Devon Fire & Rescue Service | 17 Newton Rd-Torquay<br>FL10-Angloco-Bronto 28-2TI |
| J43SOF | 121 | ALP | 92 | | West Midlands Fire Service | C7 Icknield Port Rd-Ladywood<br>**Temp move C4 Bournbrook due to H204MOK at Simon's.**  FL10-Saxon-Simon ST300-S-**ST290-S** |
| J561PND | | ALP | 92 | | Greater Manchester County Fire Service | **ex A10 Liverpool Rd-Salford-1996**/ Reserve-<br>FL10-Bedwas-Simon ST290-S |
| J915MJX | 002 | HP | 92 | | West Yorkshire Fire Service | BD Nelson St-Bradford<br>FL6-18-Bedwas-Simon SS263 |
| J916MJX | 001 | HP | 92 | | West Yorkshire Fire Service | CD Skircoat Moor Rd-Halifax<br>FL6-18-Bedwas-Simon SS263 |
| NMN999 | | HP | 92 | | Isle of Man Fire & Rescue Service | 1 Peel Rd-Douglas-**Booms re chassied off ERF-NMN999**<br>FL6-17-Carmichael-Simon SS220 |

This photograph shows three aerial appliances:- H126DKG, ABO665L and B457BHB used in three different decades. These aerial appliances are based at Adam Street station in Cardiff and show how high-rise fire fighting has developed over thirty years. The 1972 ERF has HCB Angus bodywork and Simon SS85 booms. The 1984 Renault G16C has Angloco bodywork and Metz DL30 ladders while the 1990 Volvo FL10 has Saxon Bodywork and Simon ST300 booms.
*Clive Shearman*

**Hereford & Worcester's L301UWP, a Volvo FL7 with Simon SS263 Hydraulic Platform, is seen here in Redditch. The hydraulic booms were taken from an earlier Redditch-based Ford D series appliance that was new in 1977. Recently, L301UWP was transfered following changes in fire cover requirements in the north of Worcestershire the appliance is now based at Bromsgrove.**
*Clive Shearman*

| | | | | | | |
|---|---|---|---|---|---|---|
| K469PAG | | ALP | 92 | | Humberside Fire & Rescue Service | A3 Calvert Rd-Hull West<br>FL10-Bedwas-Simon ST290-S |
| K392PVL | | HP | 93 | | Lincolnshire Fire & Rescue Service | B1 Churchill Ave-Skegness<br>FL6-18 Bedwas-Simon SS263 |
| K497MSR | 1695 | ALP | 93 | | Tayside Fire Brigade<br>(Scotland) | A1 Blackness Rd-Dundee<br>FL10-Bedwas-Simon ST290-S |
| K456EMS | | ALP | 93 | | Central Region Fire Brigade-**1995**<br>Central Scotland FB (Scotland) | S8 Ranoch Rd-Stirling<br>FL10-Angloco-Bronto 28-2TI |
| K474OKB | 1293 | CPL | 93 | | Merseyside Fire Brigade | E1 Parr Stocks Rd-St Helens<br>FL10-Angloco-Bronto-28-2TI |
| K475OKB | 1294 | CPL | 93 | | Merseyside Fire Brigade | W1 Exmouth St-Birkenhead<br>FL10-Angloco-Bronto-28-2TI |
| K64XBA | | ALP | 93 | | Greater Manchester County<br>Fire Service | B27 St Helens Rd-Leigh<br>FL10-Bedwas-Simon ST290-S |
| K65XBA | | ALP | 93 | | Greater Manchester County<br>Fire Service | D40 Whithill St-Stockport<br>FL10-Bedwas-Simon ST290-S |
| K959EYH | HP18 | HP | 93 | | London Fire Brigade | H32 London Rd-Norbury-1996 / Southern Command<br>Reserve<br>**Booms re-chassied off S &Drewry WY-CFE-GYW667W**<br>FL6-18-Saxon-Simon SS220 |
| L964DJW | 123 | ALP | 93 | | West Midlands Fire Service | E1 Blue Lane West-Walsall<br>FL10-Saxon-Simon ST300-S |
| NDZ7068 | | ALP | 93 | | Northern Ireland Fire Brigade | A01 Bankmore St-Belfast<br>FL10-Angloco-Bronto 28-2TI |
| L301UWP | | HP | 93 | | Hereford & Worcester Fire Brigade | ND 27 Birmingham Rd-Redditch-1996<br>ND 25 Windsor St-Bromsgrove-<br>**Booms re chassied off Ford-WUY322R**<br>FL7-Angloco-Simon SS263 |
| L81RTP | | TL | 94 | | Hampshire Fire & Rescue Service | C30 North Walls-Winchester<br>FL6-18-Angloco-Metz DLK30 |
| L21XEY | | ALP | 94 | | County of Clwyd Fire Service-**1996**<br>North Wales Fire Service (Wales) | W1/C03 Coast Rd-Rhyl<br>FL10-Angloco-Bronto F30 HDT |
| M163PFO | | ALP | 94 | | Powys Fire Service-**1996**<br>Mid & West Wales FB (Wales) | 13/N13 Tremont Rd-Llandrindod Wells<br>FL6-18 Angloco-Bronto F24 HDT |
| M164SWL | | HP | 95 | | Buckinghamshire Fire & Rescue<br>Service | Skelton Close-Beaconsfield<br>**Booms re chassied off Dennis F135 UVS197W**<br>FL6-18-Angloco-Simon SS220 |
| M451KOV | 124 | ALP | 95 | | West Midlands Fire Service | E5 Merridale St-Wolverhampton<br>FL10-Saxon-Simon ST290-S |
| SDZ5029 | | TL | 95 | | Northern Ireland Fire Brigade | Springfield Fire Station<br>FS7-18-Dennison-Magirus DL30 |
| N597GLF | | ALP | 95 | | Surrey Fire & Rescue Service | 33 Addlestone Moor-Chertsey<br>FL10-Angloco-Bronto F32 HDT |
| N598GLF | | ALP | 95 | | Surrey Fire & Rescue Service | 22 By-Pass Ladymead-Guilford<br>FL10-Angloco-Bronto F32 HDT |
| N599GLF | | ALP | 95 | | Surrey Fire & Rescue Service | ED 13 Cobham Rd-Leatherhead<br>FL10-Angloco-Bronto F32 HDT |
| N192SDA | 125 | ALP | 96 | | West Midlands Fire Service | D2 Dudley Rd-Brierley Hill<br>FL10-Saxon-Simon ALP 340 |
| N991OHV | HP19 | HP | 96 | | London Fire Brigade | H43 South Rd-Twickenham<br>**Booms re-chassied off S &Drewry WY-CFE-GYW664W**<br>FL6-18-Angloco-Simon SS220 |
| N992OHV | HP20 | HP | 96 | | London Fire Brigade | E22 Blissett St-Greenwich<br>**Booms re-chassied off S &Drewry WY-CFE-GYW665W**<br>FL6-18-Saxon-Simon SS220 |
| N993OHV | HP21 | HP | 96 | | London Fire Brigade | H32 London Rd-Norbury<br>**Booms re-chassied off S &Drewry WY-CFE-KUV697X**<br>FL6-18-Saxon-Simon SS220 |

| | | | | | | |
|---|---|---|---|---|---|---|
| N432RCN | 065 | ALP | 96 | | Durham Fire & Rescue Brigade | G1 Finchale Rd-Framwellgate Moor-Durham FL10-Angloco-Bronto F32HDT |
| N65DEM | 1310 | CPL | 96 | | Merseyside Fire Brigade | N3 Storrington Ave-Croxteth-Liverpool FL10-Angloco-Bronto F32 HDT |
| N374YNC | | ALP | 96 | | Greater Manchester County Fire Service | A10 Liverpool Rd-Salford FL10 Saxon-Simon ST290-S |
| N375YNC | | ALP | 96 | | Greater Manchester County Fire Service | C36 The Rock-Bury FL10 Saxon-Simon ST290-S |
| N376YNC | | ALP | 96 | | Greater Manchester County Fire Service | E50 Thompson St Manchester Central FL10 Saxon-Simon ST290-S |
| N377YNC | | ALP | 96 | | Greater Manchester County Fire Service | E54 Hodgeson St-Ashton under Lyne FL10 Saxon-Simon ST290-S |
| P752TSU | | ALP | 96 | | Strathclyde Fire Brigade (Scotland) | **New A7 Maryhill Fire Station** FL10-Angloco-Bronto F32 HDT |
| P418CAL | | TL | 96 | | Nottinghamshire Fire & Rescue Service | 18 Shakespeare St-Nottingham FL6-18-Angloco Metz DLK30 |
| P462RHV | HP22 | HP | 97 | | London Fire Brigade | **Booms Re-chassied off S& Drewry WY-CFE-GYW669W** FL6-18-Saxon-Simon SS220 |
| P463RHV | HP23 | HP | 97 | | London Fire Brigade | **Booms Re-chassied off S & Drewry WY-CFE-KUV695X** FL6-18-Saxon-Simon SS220 |
| P550WHG | 30 | ALP | 97 | | Lancashire County Fire Brigade | **? Preston** FL10-Angloco-Bronto F32 HDT |
| P551WHG | 30 | ALP | 97 | | Lancashire County Fire Brigade | **? Blackburn** FL10 Angloco-Bronto F32 HDT |

| | | | | | Volvo Chassied Specialist Appliances | |
|---|---|---|---|---|---|---|
| D128ERW | | PMover BAU LTU | 87 | | Mid Glamorgan Fire Service-**1996** South Wales Fire Service (Wales) | **ex 01 Bridgend-1993** 17 Cwmbach Rd-Aberdare FL6-14-Powell Duffryn |
| D129ERW | | PMover CIU | 87 | | Mid Glamorgan Fire Service-**1996** South Wales Fire Service (Wales) | **ex 15 Pontypridd-1992** 10 Llwynpia Rd-Tonypandy FL6-14-Powell Duffryn |
| E177SUH | | PMover | 87 | | Mid Glamorgan Fire Service-**1996** South Wales Fire Service (Wales) | Training Department FL6-17-Brimac |
| E902WUD | B10W | WRC | 88 | | Oxfordshire Fire & Rescue Service | B10 Slade Park-Oxford **Tank off Dodge K1613-XRO615S ex Bedfordshire** FL6-17-HCB Angus-Frazer Engineering |
| E993AHH | 07-02 | FOT | 88 | | Cumbria Fire Service | CD Warwick St-Carlisle FL6-14-Carmichael |
| E997AHH | 07-03 | FOT | 88 | | Cumbria Fire Service | AD Hessingham-Whitehaven FL6-14-Carmichael |
| E175DVH | | Rec/V | 88 | | West Yorkshire Fire Service | Brigade Workshops FL7-Safrec-Bro Wrecker |
| MAN999B | | HLL FOT | 88 | | Isle of Man Fire & Rescue Service | 1 Peel Rd-Douglas FL10-Nova Scotia |
| F143FWL | | PM /FOT CU/CIU Salv/T | 89 | | Royal Berkshire Fire & Rescue Service | 20 Whitley Wood Rd-Reading FL6-17-Acoma/Wilsdon/Fergussons |
| F611BAV | | PM/SIU ICCU | 89 | | Cambridgeshire Fire & Rescue Service | A27 Hartford Rd-Huntingdon FL6-17-F&Wylie |
| F612BAV | | HazM SRU | 89 | | Cambridgeshire Fire & Rescue Service | **ex B13-Huntingdon-1992** **Prime Mover-Fitted HIAB 050 crane** / B13-St Neot's FL6-17-John Dennis CB |
| E346CVK F843JBB | 443 | ET | 88 | | Tyne & Wear Fire Brigade | T Victoria Rd West-Hebburn- EDK Keppel St-South Shields-  **Winch fitted** FL6-14-F&Wylie |

| | | | | | | |
|---|---|---|---|---|---|---|
| G435VFE | | ETCU | 89 | | Lincolnshire Fire & Rescue Service | D1 Harlaxton Rd-Grantham-Control Unit FL6-14-Saxon |
| G922-7TYN J928/9CYP K960-2EYH L21/3-4GYK M996-90LYP P465/6RHV | HDC-23/7 HDC-28/9 HDC-30/2 HDC-33/5 HDC-36/9 HDC-40/1 | HDC | 89/ 90 92 93 94 95 96 | | In 1986 the **London Fire Brigade** purchased its first Volvo chassis which would provide the backbone of the fleet  through the 90s. The locations and types of pods carried are to varied and diverse to note here. | FL6-14-Locomotors FL6-14-Arlington FL6-14-King & Taylor FL6-14-Locomotors FL6-14-Hilbrow FL6-14-Saxon -FL6-14-Saxon |
| G162UPO | | Special Eqp/U | 90 | | Hampshire Fire Service | A01 West Ham Close-Basingstoke Control Unit FL6-14-HFS |
| G163UPO | | Special Eqp/U | 90 | | Hampshire Fire Service | D54 St Marys Rd-St Mary's-Southampton-**Control Unit** FL6-14-HFS |
| G350FCP | 115 | ET | 90 | | West Yorkshire Fire Service | **ex A Div Kikstall Rd-Leeds-1995**/ A24 Gipton-Leeds- FL6-08-Devcoplan |
| G351FCP | 116 | ET | 90 | | West Yorkshire Fire Service | **ex C Div Skircoat Rd-Halifax-1995**/ C60-Huddersfield- FL6-08-Devcoplan |
| H135OKG | | PM /ICU DCU BaT CAV | 90 | | South Glamorgan Fire & Rescue-1996 South Wales Fire Service (Wales) | 01 Adam St-Central-Cardiff FL6-14-Rolonoff |
| H178UCX | 117 | Heavy Res/T | 91 | | West Yorkshire Fire Service | **ex CD Hightown-Cleckheaton-1993** B Div Highfield Rd-Idle-Bradford FL6-14-WYFS |
| H851XYF | FRU-1 | FRU | 91 | | London Fire Brigade | E21 Lewisham High St-Lewisham-1996 H37 Este Rd-Battersea FL6-14-Carmichael |
| H852XYF | FRU-2 | FRU | 91 | | London Fire Brigade | H31 Old Town-Croydon FL6-14-Carmichael |
| H853XYF | FRU-3 | FRU | 91 | | London Fire Brigade | A23 Euston Rd-Euston-1995 / A29-Barbican-1995/6 A21 Harrow Rd-Paddington FL6-14-Carmichael |
| H854XYF | FRU-4 | FRU | 91 | | London Fire Brigade | G38-London Rd-Heston FL6-14-Carmichael |
| H654ECU | U21 | PM /CIU ICCU | 91 | | Northumberland Fire & Rescue Service | A01Loansdean-Morpeth FL6-17-Multilift-Penman |
| H482TRM | 07-04 | FOT | 91 | | Cumbria Fire Service | BD Abbey Rd-Barrow in Furness FL6-14-Carmichael |
| H486TRM | 05-07 | Major/RV | 91 | | Cumbria Fire Service | A Div King St-Workington FL6-14-Carmichael |
| H826DVL | | ETCU | 91 | | Lincolnshire Fire & Rescue Service | C1 Robin Hoods Walk-Boston-**Control Unit** FL6-14-Saxon |
| J935CYP | FRU-5 | FRU | 91 | | London Fire Brigade | F44 High St-East Ham FL6-14-Carmichael |
| J936CYP | FRU-6 | FRU | 91 | | London Fire Brigade | A39 North Circular Rd-Finchley-1994 / A34-Edmonton FL6-14-Carmichael |
| J561XAW | 102 | PMover EFU | 91 | | Shropshire Fire & Rescue Service | Stafford Park-Telford Central FL6-14-Torton |
| J83CTS | | ET | 92 | | Fife Fire & Rescue Service (Scotland) | A4 Lumphinnans Rd-Lochgelly FL6-14-Reliance Mercury |
| J641HFW | | ETCU | 92 | | Lincolnshire Fire & Rescue Service | B1 Churchill Ave-Skegness-**Control Unit** FL6-14-Saxon |
| J712NWL | | OSU | 92 | | Buckinghamshire Fire & Rescue Service | St Marys St-High Wycombe FL6-14-Chambers Engineering |
| J703RRO | 16 | WRC | 92 | | Bedfordshire  Fire & Rescue Service | 10 Dunstable Rd-Toddington FL7-Saxon |
| J824MFC | 15 | WRC | 92 | | Bedfordshire Fire & Rescue Service | 12 Southfields Rd-Kempston FL7-Saxon |
| J791GJX | 118 | PMover HazM | 92 | | West Yorkshire Fire Service | D83 Huddersfield Rd-Dewsbury FL6-17-Multilift-Locomotors-Powell-Duffryn |

| | | | | | | |
|---|---|---|---|---|---|---|
| J792GJX WY1 | 119 | PMover Major/RT | 92 | | West Yorkshire Fire Service | C62 Hightown Rd-Cleckheaton/**Carries ET kit off-G351FCP** FL6-18-Multilift-Leicester Carriage-Powell Duffryn |
| K592SJX | 121 | PMover ISU | 92 | | West Yorkshire Fire Service | **ex D91 Carlton Lane-Rothwell-1995**/ D Reserve-FL6-18-Multilift-Locomotors-Powell Duffryn |
| K593SJX | 122 | PMover HLL | 92 | | West Yorkshire Fire Service | B40 Nelson St-Bradford FL6-18-Multilift-Machook-Powell Duffryn |
| 999GMN | | HRU | 92 | | Isle of Man Fire & Rescue Service | 1 Peel Rd-Douglas - FL6-14-Penman-Outreach-**Palfinger 8000 crane fitted** |
| K720BUJ | 2 | PMover ISU | 92 | | Shropshire Fire & Rescue Service | Stafford Park-Telford Central FL6-14-Torton |
| K182MPO | | ETCU | 92 | | Hampshire Fire & Rescue Service | B20 Copner Rd-Copner-Portsmouth FL6-14-HF&RS |
| K141SBX | | PM /WRC BAT | 93 | | Dyfed County Fire Brigade-**1996** Mid & West Wales FB (Wales) | A1/W1 Corporation Ave-Llanelli FS7-18-Dairy Products-Leicester Carriage |
| K102UJO | | OSU | 93 | | Buckinghamshire Fire & Rescue Service | Sherwood Drive-Bletchley-Milton Keynes FL6-14-Chambers |
| K103UJO | | WRC | 93 | | Buckinghamshire Fire & Rescue Service | New Rd-Princes Risborough-**Converted to Snozzle** FL6-17-Dairy Crest |
| K907VRU | | WRC | 93 | | Dorset Fire Brigade | B15 Worget Rd-Wareham- **Tank off Leyland RYA679R** FL6-18-Boughton |
| K706LYJ | | WRC | 93 | | East Sussex Fire Brigade | 13 Beacon Rd-Crowborough FS7-18-Maidment |
| L515XBB | 081 | PMover | 94 | | Durham County Fire Brigade | Training Centre FL6-17-Multilift |
| L184VTN | 163 | Salv/T | 94 | | Tyne & Wear Fire Brigade | J Preston Rd North-Tynemouth FS7-JDC-**Atlas 130.1 Crane** |
| L728EJX | 097 | PMover | 94 | | West Yorkshire Fire Service | A26 Stongate Rd-Moortown-Leeds FL6-18-Multilift-Machook |
| L729EJX | 099 | PMover | 94 | | West Yorkshire Fire Service | Training Centre/Reserve FL6-18-Multilift-Machook |
| L106JNT | 8 | PMover HPU | 94 | | Shropshire Fire & Rescue Service | St Micheals St-Shrewsbury -**Heavy Pumping Unit** FL6-18- Mcdonald Kane-Genetech-**Hydro Sub Mote Pump** |
| L107JNT | 9 | PMover HRU | 94 | | Shropshire Fire & Rescue Service | St Micheals St-Shrewsbury-**Hose Recovery Unit** FL6-18-Mcdonald Kane-Genetech-**1 km hose** |
| L961DJW | 309 | PM /MRU FDU/ ISU | 94 | | West Midlands Fire Service | B7 Northway-NEC Bickenhill FS7-18-Keyway-Buckingham |
| L962DJW | 310 | PM /MRU ISU/FDU | 94 | | West Midlands Fire Service | D8 Hargate Lane-West Bromwich FS7-18-Keyway-Buckingham |
| L351HNV | 27 | ET OSU | 94 | | Bedfordshire Fire & Rescue Service | 13 Stopsley Way-Stopsley-Luton FL6-18-Bedwas |
| L607KUD | 28 | ET OSU | 94 | | Bedfordshire Fire & Rescue Service | 12 Southfields Rd-Kempston FL6-18-Bedwas |
| L202ANL | 167 | ET | 94 | | Tyne & Wear Fire Brigade | D Pilgrim St-Newcastle Central FL6-14-HCB Angus |
| L627YDX | R00005 | PMover | 94 | | Suffolk Fire Service | 01 Colchester Rd-Ipswich FL6-14 Powell Duffryn |
| L628YDX | R00006 | PMover | 94 | | Suffolk Fire Service | 01 Colchester Rd-Ipswich FL6-14 Powell Duffryn |
| M267XOT | | WRC Foam/C | 95 | | Hampshire Fire & Rescue Service | C29 Eastleigh -1996 / A01 West Ham Close-Basingstoke FL7-Locomotors-**Rebodied by Angloco's** |
| M830JAX | | OSU | 95 | | South Glamorgan Fire & Rescue-**1996** South Wales Fire Service (Wales) | 06 Hazel Rd-Penarth FL7-Bedwas-Moffat |
| M656TWL | A6R | Res/T | 95 | | Oxfordshire Fire & Rescue Service | A6 Sterling Rd-Kidlington FL6-14-Excalibur CBK |
| M128BPN | | Heavy Rec/V | 95 | | East Sussex Fire & Rescue Service | A01 North St-Lewes FL6-14-W H Bence-**HIAB 071 Crane** |
| M415FRG | 084 | Heavy Rec/V | 95 | | Durham County Fire & Rescue Service | N1 Watling St-Bishop Auckland FL10-Boniface Engineering |

| | | | | | | |
|---|---|---|---|---|---|---|
| M660KDW | | PMover Canteen | 95 | | Mid Glamorgan Fire Service-**1996** South Wales Fire Service (Wales) | 14 Llantrisant Rd-Pontyclun FL6-14-Lacre |
| M671GVL | | PMover | 95 | | Lincolnshire Fire & Rescue Service | D1 Harlaxton Rd-Grantham FL6-14 Powell Duffryn Rolonof-**Hiab 071 Crane** |
| M452KOV | 3305 | PMover | 95 | | West Midlands Fire Service | C9 Speedwell Rd-Hay Mills FS7-Multilift |
| M453KOV | 306 | PMover | 95 | | West Midlands Fire Service | E3 Clarks Lane-Willenhall FS7-18-Multilift |
| M232YBG | 1308 | PMover BF/Unit | 95 | | Merseyside Fire Brigade | E1 Parr Stocks Rd-St Helens FS7-18-Cargotec-Multilift |
| M233YBG | 1309 | PMover BF/Unit | 95 | | Merseyside Fire Brigade | W6 Mill Lane Wallesey FS7-18-Cargotec-Multilift |
| M557KVK N389RCN | 229 | ET | 95 | | Tyne & Wear Metropolitan Fire Brigade | N Railway Rd-Sunderland FL6-14-Excalibur CBK |
| N117EBP | | Foam Water/C | 96 | | Hampshire Fire & Rescue Service | C29 Steele Close-Eastleigh FL7-Angloco |
| N576ASX | | ES/Unit | 96 | | Fife Fire & Rescue Service (Scotland) | A6 Castle Rd-Rosyth FL6-14-Penman |
| N530WRM | 05-08 | Major/RV | 96 | | Cumbria Fire Service | CD Warwick St-Carlisle FL6-14-Emergency One |
| N344VUX | 11 | Heavy Rec/V | 96 | | Shropshire Fire & Rescue Service | Wellington FL6-14-Saxon-**Hiab 071 Crane** |
| N765YEF | | Control Unit | 96 | | North Yorkshire Fire & Rescue Service | E11 Crosby Rd-Northalllerton FL6-14-Bailey's Totalfleet-North Yorkshire F&RS |
| N812WAV | | Command Unit | 96 | | Cambridgeshire Fire & Rescue Service | A27 Hartford Rd-Huntingdon FL6-14-Leicester Carriage Builders |
| N478VMS | | Command Unit | 96 | | Central Scotland Fire Brigade (Scotland) | F1 Linlithgow Rd-Bowness FL6-14-Heggies of Cupar |
| N530WRM | 05-09 | Major/RV | 97 | | Cumbria Fire Service | Warwick Street-Carlisle FL6-14-Emergency One |
| P21GNA | | IC/Unit | 97 | | Greater Manchester County Fire Service | A12 Bolton Rd-Agecroft B6-9.9m-Saxon-Northern Counties |

Photographed at Prees, Shropshire was then-new Heavy Rescue Tender N344VUX. The appliance is normally allocated to Wellington station, where it is more central to the counties road system, and the M54. The unit is fitted with a Hiab 071 crane capable of handling this growing type of rescue.
*Clive Shearman*

# MISCELLANEOUS TELESCOPING BOOMED AERIAL APPLIANCES

| Reg No | Fleet No | TYPE | YR | OS | Appliance & Brigade Name | Details/Stations |
|--------|----------|------|----|----|--------------------------|------------------|
| Type Mk1 Mk2 Mk2A | Engine 4.2 litre P 6.5 litre P V8 diesel | Boom 31.5' 45' 45' | | | Details 200gW/900 gpmP 300gW/1000 gpmP 300gW/1000 gpmP | Scoosher is an old Glasgow slang term for ' water pistol' and a scoosh to a Glasgow fireman means to give a quick wash down with a jet. All the below Glasgow appliances passed to Strathclyde Fire Brigade. |
| TSM | | 15m | | | | TSM stands for ' Telescoping Simoniter ' which was a 15 metre boomed arm. |
| SGE700G | | Scoosher | 69 | ? | Glasgow Fire Service (Scotland) | A2 Soho St-East-**Replaced by B8 Calton**-D-Bennett-Simon Mk1 |
| SGE701G | | Scoosher | 69 | ? | Glasgow Fire Service (Scotland) | B5 Queens Park Fire Station-**Replaced by B5 Polmadie-1985** D-Bennett-Simon Mk1 |
| SGE702G | | Scoosher | 69 | ? | Glasgow Fire Service (Scotland) | C4/A07 Kelvinhaugh St-West-1974 A8 Anderston Fire Station-1980 /F05 Craigdhu Milngavie-D-Bennett-Simon Mk1 |
| WGA714H | | Scoosher | 70 | ? | Glasgow Fire Service (Scotland) | B2 Govan Rd-Govan /F24 Argyll St Dunoon-Dennis F46A-Bennett-Simon Mk2 |
| WGD613H | | Scoosher | 70 | ? | Glasgow Fire Service (Scotland) | A4/A02 Grudie St-Easterhouse Dennis F46A-Bennett-Simon Mk2 |
| XGE211J | | Scoosher | 71 | ? | Glasgow Fire Service (Scotland) | C5/A09 North Fire Station Dennis F46A-Bennet-Simon Mk2 |
| XGE212J | | Scoosher | 71 | ? | Glasgow Fire Service (Scotland) | A5/A03 Petershill-Springburn Dennis F46A-Bennett-Simon Mk2 |
| XGE213J | | Scoosher | 71 | ? | Glasgow Fire Service (Scotland) | A1 Ingram St-Central A01 Port Dundas Rd-Cowcaddens Dennis F46A-Bennett-Simon Mk2 |
| KTD615K | 91 2714 | Simoniter FOT | 71 | 89 | Lancashire County Fire Brigade | E70 Broadway-Chadderton-1974 C35 Broadway-Chadderton-1979-Greater Manchester CFS **Sold to Angloco's Ltd-1986** **Sold to West Yorkshire Fire Service** E14 Corporation St-Morley **Booms re mounted onto Volvo FL6-14-F848SHD** Ford D1616-HCB Angus-Simon TSM15 |
| XBA327K | 59 | Simoniter | 71 | **78?** | City of Liverpool | #17/C3 Canning Place-Wapping-**Written off in RTA** F49-Dennis-Simon TSM15 |
| ATB215L | 189 | Simoniter | 72 | 81 | Lancashire County Fire Brigade | D63 Windermere Drive-Leigh-1974 B27 Windermere Drive-Leigh-1981/Greater Manchester CFS D1616-HCB Angus-Simon TSM15 |
| GGA154L | | Scoosher | 73 | ? | Glasgow Fire Service (Scotland) | C2/A05 Anniesland Rd-Knightswood Dodge K850 Tricentrol-Carmichael-Simon Mk2A |
| GGA155L | | Scoosher | 73 | ? | Glasgow Fire Service (Scotland) | B3 Leverside Crescent-Pollok F15 Sinclair Drive-Oban Dodge K850 Tricentrol-Carmichael-Simon Mk2A |
| GGE394L | | Scoosher | 73 | ? | Glasgow Fire Service (Scotland) | B1 South Fire Station-1980 Dodge K850 Tricentrol-Carmichael-Simon Mk2A |
| GGE395L | | Scoosher | 73 | ? | Glasgow Fire Service (Scotland) | C3/A6 Partick Fire Station Dodge K850 Tricentrol-Carmichael-Simon Mk2A |
| GYS175L | | Scoosher | 73 | ? | Glasgow Fire Service (Scotland) | C4/A07 Kelvinhaugh St-West/**Sold to Vehicle Finders Ltd** Dodge K850 Tricentrol-Carmichael-Simon Mk2A |
| GYS176L | | Scoosher | 73 | ? | Glasgow Fire Service (Scotland) | B4 Raithburn Ave-Castlemilk /C11 George Rd Gourock-Dodge K850 Tricentrol-Carmichael-Simon Mk2A |

| | | | | | | |
|---|---|---|---|---|---|---|
| VWR676L | | Simoniter | 73 | | West Riding of Yorkshire Fire Brigade | Saltaire Rd-Shipley-1974<br>A19 Saltaire Rd-Shipley-West Yorkshire Fire Service<br>K1050-Jennings-Simon TSM15 |
| AVW980L | | Simoniter FOT | 72 | 89 | Essex County Fire Brigade | B27/C52 Broadmayne-Basildon<br>Dennis F48-Dennis-Simon TSM15 |
| SDM391M | | Simoniter | 73 | 89 | County of Flintshire Fire Brigade (Wales) | Coast Rd-Rhyl-1974/ W1 Coast Rd-Rhyl-1980<br>E6 Chester Rd-Flint-1989/County of Clwyd Fire Brigade<br>**Preserved for the National Fire Service Museum**<br>F48-Dennis-Simon TSM15 |
| YVU133M | | Simoniter | 73 | 84 | City of Manchester | Birch St-Gorton-1974/ E53 Birch St-Gorton-1984<br>Greater Manchester CFS/**Preserved**<br>ERF 84RF-Jennings-Simon TSM15 |
| RUP530M | | Simoniter | 74 | 83 | Durham County Fire Brigade | C1/S1 St Cuthberts Way-Darlington<br>Dennis F48-Dennis-Simon TSM15 |
| MAR799P | | Simoniter FOT | 76 | 87 | Essex County Fire Brigade | B30/C50 Hogg Lane-Grays<br>Dennis F48-Dennis-Simon TSM15 |
| LOW465R | | Simoniter | 76 | 83 | Hampshire Fire Brigade | D58 Falconer Crt-Fawley-1983<br>**Converted Recovery Vehicle**-Brigade Workshops<br>Dodge K1113-HCB Angus-Simon TSM15m |
| F848SHD | | Simoniter FOT | 89 | 96 | West Yorkshire Fire Service | A27 Corporation St-Morley<br>**Booms Re-chassied off Ford D1000-KTD615K**<br>Volvo FL6-14-WYFS-Simon TSM15 |
| K103UJO | | Snozzle | 93 | | Buckinghamshire Fire & Rescue | Cambridge St-Aylesbury<br>**Chassis used from former Water Carrier**<br>FL6-17-GB Fire-Snozzle P-50 |

Seen in the drill yard of St Cuthberts Way, Darlington is RUP530M, with Tele Simoniter. It spent all its time working out of this Durham station before being sold in 1983. There were only 10 Simoniters to see active service around the United Kingdom, including one which was placed on an old chassis. One of the type has been preserved by the National Fire Service Museum.
*Ian Moore*

# ABBREVIATIONS

| TYPE | EXPLANATION OF ABBREVIATION | REMARKS |
|---|---|---|
| ACCU | Accident Unit | Similar to Emergency/Rescue Tender |
| AMB | Ambulance | Full Paramedic Accident/Rescue capibility |
| ALP | Aerial Ladder Platform-90' or 110' Height | Bronto Skylift **28-2TI** (29.5M) **33-2TI** & **ST300-S**(31.5M) **ST240-S** (25.5M)**ST290-S** (31 M) |
| **Argocat** | Argocat | 6 Wheel Drive off road vehicle |
| BAT | Breathing Apparatus Tender | Can service Breathing Apparatus sets on scene |
| **BL/RECV** | Breakdown or Recovery Vehicle/Lorry | |
| **B/WRC** | Bulk Water Carrier | Large Water Carrier |
| CAV | Canteen Van | Salvation Army or Brigade run. |
| CIU | Chemical Incident Unit | Carries full Decontamination/Showering facilities. |
| CPL | Compact Platform Ladder | Same as **APL** |
| CRT | Crash Rescue Tender | Foam/Water Capibility |
| CRU | Cliff Rescue Unit/Tender | Carry's line's/winches/stretcher's |
| CSU | Command Support Unit | Normally a small Control Unit-backs up main unit |
| **CU/COMMU** | Control Unit/Command Unit | Attends 5+ Pump Fire/Incident's |
| DCU | Damage Control Unit | Salvage/Drying/Security equipment |
| DU | Decontamination Unit | Attends Radioactive/Chemical Incident's |
| EP | Emergeney Pump's | Green Goddess .Auxillary Fire Service machines. |
| ERA | Emergency Rescue Appliance | Similar to Emergency/Rescue Tender |
| ESU | Emergency Support Unit | Similar to **HRT/MRT/RES/U** etc |
| ET | Emergency Tender | Carries winches/spreader's/cutting gear inc **Holmatro/Zumro/Turfor/Kango/Clan Lukas** |
| FCU | Forward Control Unit | Can be mounted on a 4x4 chassis. |
| FOC | Foam Carrier/Tanker | Bulk Foam Carrier |
| FBT | Fire Boat | |
| **F/HL** | Foam Hose Layer | Combination Vehicle |
| FIU | Fire Investigation Unit | Carries fire investigators to incidents/Equipment |
| FOT | Foam Tender | Some can be in pod form |
| FPU | Fire Prevention Unit | Attends after the incident is over. |
| **F/SALV** | Foam/Salvage Tender | Machine with dual role. |
| **H/FOT** | Hose Layer/Foam Tender | Machine with dual role. |
| **Hi-ex FT** | High Expansion Foam Tender | Carries Foam making materials. |
| HLL | Hose Laying Lorry | Contains approx 3 miles of hose on rack's |
| HP | Hydraulic Platform | **SS50**(50') **SS65**(65') **SS70**(70') **SS85**(85') **SS220**(77') **SS263**(91') **SS300**(103') **Orbitor** booms 72' |
| HRT | Hose Reel Tender | Term not used today/replaced by WRT |
| HRT | Heavy Rescue Tender | Same as **ET / MRT / RES/ISU** |

| ISU | Incident Support Unit | Same as **ET/MRT** /carries extra salvage/chemical equipment |
|---|---|---|
| L2P | Light 2wheel Drive Vehicle with Pump | Ford Transit/Sherpa Freight Rover etc |
| L4P/L6P | Light 4/6wheel Drive Vehicle with Pump | Land Rover/Range Rover/Pinzgaur/Uni-mog etc |
| L4T | Light 4Wheel Drive Vehicle with Hose reel | Land Rover/Austin Gypsey etc |
| L4V | Light 4wheel Drive Vehicle | Land Rover/Pinzgaur etc |
| LU | Lighting Unit | Rare most **WRL/WRT** have stem mast's. |
| MRT | Major Rescue Tender | Similar to Emergency/Rescue Tenders |
| Mini WRT | Mini Water Tender | WRT on smaller chasis |
| MW | Mobile Workshops | Often has towing facility. |
| OSU | Operational Support Unit | Same as **ET / MRT / RES/SU / HRT / ISU** |
| PUMP | Pump | Pump with 30'/35' extension ladder. |
| PE | Pump Escape | Pump with 50' wheeled ladder. |
| PHP | Pump Hydraulic Platform | Pump with 50'/60' Simon platform. |
| PL | Pump Ladder | Pump with 45' extension ladder. |
| P/FOT | Pump Foam Tender | Pump with foam making capibility/monitor. |
| PM | Prime Mover/Pod System | Pod's of all type's **CU/CIU/REST/FOT**etc. |
| PRL | Pump Rescue Ladder | Same as **WRL/R** |
| RAV | Road Accident Vehicle | Similar to Emergency/Rescue Tender |
| RES/SU | Rescue Support Unit | Same as **REST/Possibly fitted HIAB/Paflinger crane** |
| REST | Rescue Tender | Carry same equipment as **ET/MRT** but in smaller form. |
| RIV | Rapid Intervention Vehicle | First strike vehicle/Rescue capibility |
| RRU | Road Rescue Unit | Similar to Rescue Tender |
| SALV | Salvage Tender | Salvage only/Sheets/Driers/Vacums etc |
| SCOHR | Scoosher | Scottish slang term for 'Water Pistol'. A Scottish Tele boomed appliance. |
| SEA/EQT | Sea Equipment Tender | Carries Boat and equipment relevent to maritime rescue. |
| SIMTR | Simoniter | Pump with a Simon 15m Telescopic Boom. |
| SRV | Special Rescue Vehicle | Similar to Emergency/Rescue Tender |
| TL | Turntable Ladder | 100' / 125' / 150' / |
| TLP | Turntable Ladder Pump | 1,000 GPM Pump fitted. |
| TSU | Technical Support Unit | Similar to Emergency/Rescue Tender |
| WRA | Water Appliance | Same as the **WRT.** |
| WRU | Water Relay Unit | Appliance with added hose and heavy pumping capacity. |
| WRC | Water Carrier/Bowser | 5,000 Gallon's.Can be fitted with 1,000 gp. |
| WRL | Water Ladder | **WRT** with 45' extension ladder. |
| WRL/R | Water Ladder/Rescue | as above .Also rescue equipment carried. |
| WRT | Water Tender | **WRT** with 30/35' extension ladder. |
| WRT/E | Water Tender/Escape | **WRT** with 35/50' wheeled escape ladder. |
| WRT/L | Water Tender/Ladder | **WRT** with 35'/45' extension ladder. |
| WRT/R | Water Tender/Rescue | As **WRL/R** but with 35' extension ladder. |

© *British Bus Publishing* **Ltd, September 1997 - ISBN 1 897990 49 9 - The Vyne, 16 St Margarets Drive, Wellington, Telford, TF1 3PH**

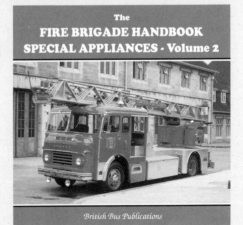